INSTRUCTOR'S SOLUTIONS MANUAL

PROJECT MANAGEMENT

Processes, Methodologies, and Economics

SECOND EDITION

Avraham Shtub · Jonathan F. Bard · Shlomo Globerson

PEARSON

Prentice Hall

Upper Saddle River, New Jersey 07458

Executive Editor: *Eric Svendsen*
Editorial Assistant: *Andrea Messineo*
Executive Managing Editor: *Vince O'Brien*
Managing Editor: *David A. George*
Production Editor: *Wendy Kopf*
Supplement Cover Manager: *Daniel Sandin*
Manufacturing Buyer: *Lisa McDowell*

© 2005 by Pearson Education, Inc.
Pearson Prentice Hall
Pearson Education, Inc.
Upper Saddle River, NJ 07458

Pearson Prentice Hall™ is a trademark of Pearson Education, Inc.

Printed in the United States of America

10 9 8 7 6 5 4 3 2 1

ISBN 0-13-186518-8

Pearson Education Ltd., *London*
Pearson Education Australia Pty. Ltd., *Sydney*
Pearson Education Singapore, Pte. Ltd.
Pearson Education North Asia Ltd., *Hong Kong*
Pearson Education Canada, Inc., *Toronto*
Pearson Educación de Mexico, S.A. de C.V.
Pearson Education—Japan, *Tokyo*
Pearson Education Malaysia, Pte. Ltd.
Pearson Education, Inc., *Upper Saddle River, New Jersey*

TABLE OF CONTENTS

This manual contains solutions to most of the analytic exercises at the end of each chapter, and to many of the qualitative exercises for which a wide range of answers are possible. Note that no solutions are provided for the exercises in Chapter 15, Project Termination.

At the back of the manual, we include a case study based on the construction of the Red Flag Channel—a monumental hydraulic project undertaken in the People's Republic of China—that can be used for teaching purposes. This material was written by Zhang Xiang of Huazhong University of Science and Technology.

Because of the difficulty in creating and solving so many problems, there are likely to be arithmetic and typographical errors throughout the manual. Should you find any, we would appreciate it if you brought them to our attention. We would also be grateful to receive any solutions that you or your students developed to the unsolved problems. For those who adopt the book, a partial set of PowerPoint Transparencies is available from the first author.

Avraham Shtub (shtub@ie.technion.ac.il)
Jonathan Bard (jbard@mail.utexas.edu)
Shlomo Globerson (globe@post.tau.ac.il)

CHAPTER

1. INTRODUCTION

1.1　(a) This is a mass production example. Standard windows are manufactured by special purpose equipment arranged according to the production process. The flow of material on the production line follows the routing of the product and each worker on the line performs the same operation on each unit of the product.

(b) This is a batch-oriented example. The one time order of 150 window assemblies is a batch that requires a special set up of the machines. In addition, the workers on the line will be performing specific operations in accordance with the unique design characteristics of the window subassemblies.

(c) This is a project-oriented example. The project is to design and build a facility that can supply 1,000 window assemblies per month throughout the year at minimum cost while meeting advertised quality standards.

1.2　Stage I　　Define location, food types, style (project)

Stage II　　Define goals and their relative importance: size, customer types, prices, opening hours, number of workers, cost, opening date (project)

Stage III　　Define performance measures: cooking time, serving time, cleaning time (project)

Stage IV　　a – Develop schedule
　　　　　　b – Develop budget
　　　　　　c – Design and plan
　　　　　　　　Cooking process
　　　　　　　　Serving process
　　　　　　　　Cleaning process
　　　　　　　　Design restaurant interior (division into kitchen area, serving area, etc.)
　　　　　　　　Furniture and décor
　　　　　　　　Decide on equipment
　　　　　　　　Decide on types of supplies and quantities
　　　　　　　　Plan advertisement

　　　　　　These are all part of a *project*

Stage V　　Integrate into project plan (project)

Stage VI　　Develop implementation plan: find location, begin interior construction; hire staff and train them; acquire equipment, furniture, décor; contract suppliers; develop advertising strategy (project)

– 1 –

Stage VII Monitor and control cost, schedule and technical process (project)

Stage VIII Run trials and evaluate (batch production)

Stage IX Open and run on daily basis (mass production)

1.3 Products:

1. Building blocks – needed by builders
   Alternatives: Wood, stone, metal.

2. Window drapes – privacy, blocks light
   Alternatives: blinds, shutters, tinted glass.

Services:

1. Express mail – communications
   Alternatives: messengers, fax, email

2. Buses – travel
   Alternatives: private car, taxi, train, airplane

1.4 Assumptions

1) The delivery company and driver have experience, both in delivery and predicting arrival times.

2) There are 2 drivers.

3) The truck will travel at an average speed of 41.7 mph MI/48 hr), including rest stops.

4) All roads from the origin and house are in good condition.

5 The truck will not encounter any traffic jams.

6) The truck is in good condition, and no mechanical failures will occur.

7) The truck will not be involved in an accident, etc.

If all of the above assumptions are true, then the truck will arrive on time.
If assumption 2 is false, then the arrival time will probably double.
If any of assumptions 3-7 are false, then there is no way to predict the arrival time.
If the shipment was by rail the assumptions are:
   a) The material will be loaded on time.
   b) The train will travel by continuously.
   c) The truck traveling from the unloading point to the house will travel continuously.

Generally, the rail option increases the probability of on time arrival.

1.5   There are 3 factors affecting price:
   1) Cost of materials
   2) Cost of equipment
   3) Cost manual work

   I.   If the house plans are available, then the cost of materials and equipment are known. The only uncertainty is manual work time. If the plumber is unable to predict this, then he lacks experience. Do not accept his proposal.

   II. If the plans are not available then the plumber cannot predict the material, equipment and manual work time needed. In this case a $2000 reserve for unseen expenses is reasonable.

1.6   The following data were collected in 10 trials.

Trail, n	Driving time (min), t
1	7
2	9
3	15
4	8
5	9
6	7
7	10
8	11
9	9
10	7

Mean, $\mu = 9.2$
Standard deviation, $\sigma = 2.44$
Coefficient of variation, $\mu / \sigma = 0.215$

1.7

   (a) Technological – availability of information; scheduling – time required to collect and process the information.

   (b) Technological – availability of information and equipment, scheduling, required activities and the duration of activities; cost – equipment, labor and transportation.

   (c) Scheduling – traffic jams, mechanical problems, driving conditions.

   (d) Cost – price not predictable; technological – quality and performances of the item.

1.8

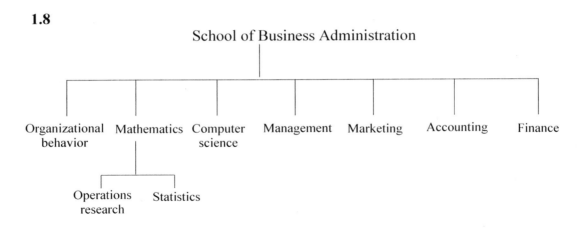

The projects in this structure are research-oriented and undertaken by teams of professors from the various departments. The product is knowledge and the publication of research results. There are several customers including the students, the local and national business community, and funding agencies.

1.9 The functional structure is identical to the structure depicted in the solution to Exercise 1.8 for the different departments in a business school.

1.10 Job description
- Appropriate education
- Previous management experience
- Communication and negotiation skills for dealing with the community, local authorities, contractors, suppliers, experts, and workers
- A member of the community (desirably a parent)

Criteria
- Relevant college degree
- 5 years of experience in a related area
- A good interview

Candidate 1
    Mechanical engineer
    3 years of experience in mechanical engineering
    Member of the community
    No children
    Hobbies: Basketball, hiking, stamp collecting

Candidate 2
    Aeronautical engineer
    7 years of experience managing in various computer-oriented small projects involving
        software development
    A parent
    Member of the community
    Hobbies: gardening, building model planes

Candidate 3
    Industrial engineer
    5 years experience in the car industry managing R&D projects
    A parent
    Not a member of the community
    Hobbies: skiing, music

Evaluation of candidates:

Candidate 1: Besides being a member of the community, this candidate's background does
                not match the rest of the job description. This candidate is not chosen.

Candidate 2: Although this candidate is qualified in most areas, the weak point is
                education and project management experience. The types of projects this
                candidate participated in did not involve communication negotiation and
                contracting skills. This candidate is not chosen.

Candidate 3: This candidate is not a member of the community and has not been involved
                in similar project. But his communication, negotiation and contracting skills
                will enable him to manage the experts needed and to carry out the project
                successfully. This candidate seems to be the best of the three.

1.11 The work content: Preparation of a thesis on the success of project management techniques
          including:

a. literature review (about 100 articles and 20 books) and preparation of research hypothesis
    (about 10)

b. preparation of a questionnaire (50 questions) based on hypothesis

c. interviews (200 managers in all 50 states)

d. statistical analysis of results (hypothesis testing ANOVA)

e. presentation of results to the customer (3 presentations)

f. preparation of a mailing questionnaire (to 100 companies)

g. distribution of mailing questionnaire (to 100 companies)

h. follow up phone calls (about 200 calls)

i. analysis of results

k. write up of thesis (about 100 typed pages, 30 tables and 20 figures)

l. revisions (3 major revisions, 10 minor revisions)

m. final production

Relevant criteria (and performance measure)

a. Ph.D degree in a related area (grade achieved)

b. at least 5 publications in related areas (number of publications)

c. good connections with industry (number of organization contacts)

d. high grades in English, writing (grades)

e. high grades in statistics (grades)

f. good knowledge of MS Word or a similar word processor (subjective evaluation)

g. living close by (distance)

h. has a computer and a laser printer at home (1 for both, 0.5 for computer only, 0 for none)

i. successfully completed other theses in the past (number of previous theses)

Required schedule

Task	Start time from project initiation, (months)	End time from project start, (months)
a	0	1
b	1	2
c	2	5
d	3	6
e	4	6
f	5	7
g	6	8
h	7	9
i	8	10
j	9	11
k	10	11
l	10	12
m	11	12

1.12 The best proposal will be selected based on a subjective evaluation of each candidate with respect to the relevant criteria and subjective weight given to each criteria. Each criteria will be measured on a scale from 0 (poor) to 5 (excellent). The weighted sum of scores will be the aggregate measure used for selection:

Criteria	Weight	Candidate 1	Candidate 2	Candidate 3
a	10%	3	4	3
b	5%	4	2	2
c	15%	4	4	2
d	15%	4	2	2
e	20%	3	5	3
f	5%	2	2	4
g	20%	1	4	3
h	5%	2	4	4
i	5%	4	2	2
	100%			
Weighted score =		27	29	25

Best candidate is number 2.

1.13 *Conceptual design phase* (project initiation selection and definition)
    Design a project
    Estimating the life cycle cost
    Getting customer's approval for the design

Advanced development (analysis of activities)
    Developing the network
Advanced development (project scheduling)
    Development of a calendar
    Estimating activity duration
Advanced development (project budgeting)
    Development of a budget

Detailed design phase (project organization)
    Selecting participating organizations
    Developing the WBS
    Establishing the milestones

Production phase (project execution and control)
    Execution of activities
    Managing the configuration
    Monitoring actual performance
    Development of corrective plans

Termination phase
    Recommending improvement steps

1.14

    (a) 1. Learning car mechanics in order to be able to repair my car.
            2. Bicycling to school

    (b) 1. Building my own house
            2. Repairing my old air conditioner

    (c) 1. Getting a pilot's license
            2. Buying a new car

    (d) 1. Buying an apartment
            2. Having a child

1.15

1. Development of a new robotic lab in the engineering school – this project is in the production phase. Most of the equipment has been purchased and installed, although some is still on order.

2. Moving to a new house – this project is at the conceptual design phase. The decision to move was made but the new house has yet to be selected.

1.16   NASA's Moon Landing Project

Risks (cost): Because many new and specialized devices were used, there were not a large number of suppliers to choose from. Also, because some of the technology was being developed at the time, it was impossible to pin down all the cost—the devices, components and subassemblies had not yet been made.

Technology: Much of the equipment was being developed and there had been relatively few manned space flights, and even fewer where the astronauts ventured outside the vehicle. Also, technology was not shared between the U.S. and the U.S.S.R. further reducing the knowledge base.

Schedule: Early in the program, the schedule was dependent on the adequate development of technology to enable a successful launch, landing, and re-entry of the spacecraft. After reaching a satisfactory technological level, a suitable window for launch was dependent on the position of the moon and the weather at Cape Canaveral. From the inception of the program, there was also an urgency brought on by political pressure to achieve these goals before the Soviets.

Resources: NASA had to choose how to divide its fixed budget to develop the technology for this mission as opposed to others, such as the development of a "space plane," which was shelved, only to be reincarnated years later as the space shuttle. Also, materials and systems, such as boasters, capsules, lunar landers, and fuel had to be design, built, and paid for all within the available budget.

Uncertainties: NASA, as a government agency, has to have annual approval of its budget by Congress -- a political body whose membership is constantly changing. Questions such as: Would the technologies work? Would the weather cooperate? Would the astronauts perform adequately? all lend an element of uncertainty to the program.

Other projects:

1. The logistics operation before Iraqi Freedom – the objective of this project was to transfer the required USA forces to Saudi Arabia before Desert Storm. This goal was successfully achieved.

2. The election campaign of George Bush – the objective of this project was to get Mr. Bush elected as the US president; the goal was successfully accomplished in 2000 and 2004(?).

1.17   Some examples are:

1. The "Spruce Goose" – In 1942, industrialist Henry Kaizer and the pilot and innovator Howard Hughes won a government contract for a fleet of giant flying boats to be built out of wood. World War II ended and the contract expired before the prototype was completed. Hughes continued with his own money and in November 1947, the $28 million plane flew about a mile above Long Beach Harbor on its first and final voyage. This project failed because the end of the war marked the end of the flying boat era. In addition, advances in metallurgy and engine performance superceded the need for light-weight wood aircraft.

2. In 1980, Israel Aircraft Industries began to develop the Lavi fighter. This project was mostly financed by the U.S. government, and by 1984 when the first prototype was ready, the Israeli government halted the project primarily for political reasons. The U.S. government withdrew financing because it felt that the Lavi would eat into the business of U.S. companies such as Boeing and Lockheed. The Israeli government, an annual recipient of U.S. foreign aid, was persuaded not to continue on its own.

3. Ballistic missile defense or "Star Wars" – This huge and costly project was initiated by Ronald Reagan in the late 1980s with the goal of protecting the U.S. from a nuclear attack by the former Soviet Union. The underlying technology was enormously complex, requiring lasers to be stationed on Earth-orbiting satellites and to be controlled through a sprawling computerized network of ground stations. The project was halted in the early 1990s when the U.S. congress failed to allocate funds for further development. Several reasons contributed to that decision including the collapse of the Soviet Union, widespread protests from respected experts who saw little hope of the system working, pressure to spend the funds elsewhere, and the failure of initial tests to achieve even a modicum of success. Nevertheless, in the early 2000s, President Bush reinitiated the project hoping to capitalize on new technologies and a favorable political mood in the congress.

CHAPTER

2. PROCESS APPROACH TO PROJECT MANAGEMENT

2.1   The project selected for this discussion is the Darwin Alice Springs Railway project. Information is available on the following web site:

http://www.aarc.com.au

(a) The major stakeholders are:

1. The citizens of Australia

2. The Northern Territory government

3. The South Australian governments

4. The government of Australia (the commonwealth government)

5. The Australasia railway corporation (established in 1997 by the Northern Territory and South Australian governments)

6. Contractors, subcontractors and suppliers

7. Workers on the project

(b) This was an external project performed for Australia (a joint venture between the northern Territory and the South Australian government) by the Australasian railway corporation.

(c) The most important resources used in the project were human resources, machines, measuring devices, and some raw materials.

1. Human resources. Because of the complex nature of the project, an exceptional need existed for licensed individuals and other experts. Although there was no lack of labor in the area, highly motivated and capable workers can make the difference between project success and failure.

2. Raw material needed for the project (e.g., 146,000 tons of steel rail, 2 million concrete sleepers, 2.8 million tons of ballast, 100,000 cubic meters of pre-stressed concrete and much more.)

3. Special machines. The machines played an important role because the sleepers and the steel rails were too heavy to be carried by men. The machines are the "common worker" here and workers only operate them.

4. Accurate measuring devices. If a line were one degree off from its planned bearings its terminal point would be 2.5 km inland with respect to the port of Darwin, the desired terminal point, or 2.5 km out at sea.

(d) The needs of the stakeholders:

1. The citizens of Australia

2. The Northern Territory government
3. The South Australian governments
4. The government of Australia (the commonwealth government)

The Northern Territory economy is small. It relies on world demand for mining, farming and tourism (though domestic tourism is more important than international). But the Northern Territory also has a solid base of defense and government employment, with the defense presence notably built up in the past decade.

Due to its size and its exposure to export markets, the Northern Territory's economic performance is volatile, but on average the past decade has seen it outperform the wider Australian economy in both output and job growth. That strong performance was led by mining and related activities (including some offshore), the defense build up, and the fact the Northern Territory is at an earlier stage of development, and so benefits from extra capital works (such as the Darwin-Alice railway). Recent Northern Territory economic growth has been modest, with the Defense build up moderating and tourism stagnating. The resultant slower population growth has meant little housing construction for three years. Nevertheless, other projects are expected to pick up the commercial construction slack, the global economy is recovering, and so too is the outlook for tourism.

The railway is expected to reduce the transport costs for goods from the inlands to the rapidly growing markets of East Asia and bring tourism into the inland. It is the only rail connection between South Australia and the north. Given the fact that ground transportation is less expensive than air and given the rapidly growing markets in the north, for Australia this railway has to become a success story, at least from an economic point of view.

1. The Australasian railway corporation (established in 1997 by the Northern Territory and South Australian Governments) holds exclusive rights to operate the entire line for the next 50 years.

2. Contractors, subcontractors and suppliers. These are for profit firms for which the project is a source of income and expertise.

3. Workers on the project. The workers are looking for good jobs that pay well and will allow them to develop their skills.

(e) The alternatives for the project are:

1. The road system which is already built and functional,

2. Using the sea as a transportation platform (combined with the road system for inlanders)

3. Using the airways, again combined with roads.

All three are cheaper in the short run – mainly because they already exist – but in the long run each has disadvantages that limit the volume and weight of goods that can be transported. Slower transportation rates ultimately mean higher costs. Another alternative is design a high-speed railway system that would increase throughput but be far more expensive to build and maintain. In the view of the planners, however, the conventional railway system is expected to satisfactorily meet the needs of the region (mainly industrial needs).

(f) The northern territory government ordered a comparison between the road option and the rail option and obtained the following results.

- For trucks:
    i. The average truck operating cost within the corridor is estimated at 3.26 cents/ntk (net tonnes-kilometer).
    ii. The average truck operating cost for operations outside of the corridor is estimated at 3.70 cents/ntk.

- For rail:
    i. rail operating costs were estimated using the Booz·Allen rail cost model at 1.82 cents/ntk for the operations within the corridor.
    ii. 2.75 cents/ntk for operations outside of the corridor.

In both cases, the operating costs are projected to decline by 1.5% per annum for 30 years due to (1) improvements related to economies of scale and future productivity gains, (2) changes in the fleet mix leading to increased capacity and improvements in fuel efficiency, and (3) better technology leading to better maintenance of the road vehicles, which include the following truck types: articulated 6-Axle, B-double, double road train, and triple road train.

In addition, the following savings in externalities are expected:

- Savings in road infrastructure costs is 0.770 cents/ntk for trucks operating within the Adelaide to Alice Springs corridor and 0.901 cents/ntk for trucks operating outside the corridor. The estimates are based on the Travers Morgan report.
- Savings in road accidents are estimated to be 0.183 cents/ntk for trucks operating within the corridor and 0.319 cents/ntk for trucks operating outside the corridor. These values were derived from the latest ARRB Accident costs for articulated vehicles.
- Savings from the reduction in greenhouse gas emissions is based on work by VTES (1994) on CO_2 vehicle emissions and Moffet (1991) cost estimates. The costs related to greenhouse gases for this analysis are 0.05 cents/ntk for rail and 0.10 cents/ntk for road.

Based on the analysis conducted during the study, the rationale for the selected alternative is as follows.

- The port connected to this rail is the closest one to the designated markets. This gives it an important role in Australian economy especially in the "global era" and in light of mining activities, which support the local economy.
- The existence of the line will play a key role in unlocking the development potential of the Northern Territory's largely untapped mineral reserves.

- The project makes Darwin a gate for tourism and the rail will make it easier to travel within Australia. Given the vast distances, rail is a better and more comfortable way of travel than road or air for both people. It is also more economical for goods.
- For the inland cities that will gain a gate towards the sea, the project is definitely a big boost; for the rail company it is a "win-win" situation.
- In the short run this may seem to be an expensive project but according to the analysis it will pay for itself in a few years and remain a major asset for the state and citizens.

The results of a 50-year economic evaluation using a discount rate of 5% are summarized in the table below.

Results of Economic Evaluation	
Measure	Project case ($M)
Capital costs (present value)	926
Benefits (present value)	1,737
Net present value	811
NPV/capital costs	0.88
Internal rate of return (%)	9.2
Benefit / cost	1.88

With an initial capital cost of $926 million (PV), the project yields a net benefit of $811 million, giving a benefit-to-cost ratio of 1.88 and an internal rate of return of 9.2%.

The table below provides a breakdown of the various sources of project benefits.

Source of project benefits	Project case ($M)	%
Operating costs improvements	913	53
Accident costs avoided	181	10
Avoidance of intermodal transfer costs	15	1
Road infrastructure cost savings	574	33
Greenhouse gas savings	54	3
Total	1,737	100

The primary source of benefits is the savings in operational cost for tonnage diverted to the new rail link. The reduction in road infrastructure costs due to the diversion of freight from to rail is the next major benefit source.

Sensitivity Analysis: A number of sensitivity tests were conducted and the results shown in the following able.

Sensitivity measures	NPV ($M)	NPV/C	B/C	IRR
Baseline evaluation	811	0.88	1.88	9.2%
Project rail operating costs: +10%	713	0.77	1.77	8.8%
Project rail operating Costs: – 0%	910	0.98	1.98	9.7%
Rail task: +10%	908	0.98	1.98	9.7%
Rail task: –10%	598	0.65	1.65	8.3%
Rail task: –20%	432	0.47	1.47	7.5%
Project construction costs: +10%	718	0.71	1.71	8.5%
Project construction costs: –10%	903	1.08	2.08	10.1%
Road operating costs: 0% annual decline	1425	1.54	2.54	11.2%
Road operating costs: –3% annual decline	396	0.43	1.43	7.5%
7% discount rate	310	0.35	1.35	9.2%
3% discount rate	1714	1.78	2.78	9.2%

The results show that the NPV ranges from $310 million to $1,714 million with the benefit-to-cost ratio (B/C) ranging from 1.35 to 2.78. Moreover, the internal rate of return (IRR) ranges from 7.5% to 11.2%, indicating that under all scenarios investigated the NPV of the project is positive at the selected discount rate of 5%.

(g) The risks of this project are of two types:

- Risks that may hamper the completion of the project
- Risks that might make the project to "a white elephant":

(h) The following list of risks is arranged by severity and phase.

- Pre-construction
  1. Inability to acquire the lands needed for the rail as planned.
  2. Lack of cash.
  3. Design and Over-investment – building an "overqualified" line for a faster train with the entire infrastructure involved.
  4. Subcontractor failure (bankruptcy).
  5. Insufficient raw material (mainly sleepers, steel rail and ballast)
  6. Opposition of the public due to environmental damage.

- Post-construction. While the Northwest Territory is projected to be a fast growing economy in comparison to the rest of Australia, its small size and resource strengths also point to it being a more volatile one. As a consequence, its past may not accurately reflect its future. Additional risks include:

   7. High maintenance costs.

   8. The $A rising beyond current expectations. This would have the effect of making some projects uncompetitive, putting at risk the strong investment outlook, and weakening the outlook for tourism and education exports.

   9. Darwin's proximity to potentially unstable Asian trouble spots of terrorist activities. This has diverted tourists from the Asia-Pacific and may continue to do so.

   10. The global recovery stuttering. While current signs are good, if global demand were to stagnate again the effect on the NT's resources and tourism sectors would be strongly negative.

   11. "Acts of God" – cyclones (and other natural phenomena) may be a higher risk for Darwin than for other Australian capital cities.

(i) The following steps were taken to mitigate the risks.

- Land and environmental risks. While the Austral Asia Railway Corporation coordinated the tender process and negotiations, the Northern Territory government had primary responsibility for negotiating with aboriginal Land Councils and pastoralist regarding acquisition of the corridor (with compensation payments of $A 22 million). Environmental and heritage issues had to be addressed and fencing the corridor was required.

   A draft environmental impact statement was released in 1983 and updated with a new environmental management plan in 1997. At that time, the project received environmental approval from the Northern Territory and from the commonwealth governments.

   The Northern Territory obtained Sacred Sites avoidance certificates in accordance with the Northern Territory Aboriginal Sacred Sites Act for an area of extending 200 meters on either side of the railway centre line and for the identified ballast sites outside the corridor. Various reports were commissioned to determine the likely impact of the railway on sites of archaeological and historical significance.

   The Aboriginal Areas Protection Authority has pegged all Aboriginal sites of significance and good working relationship between the Authority, Adrail and Aboriginal organizations is ensuring close cooperation throughout the project.

   The area of the Gouldian Finch Wet Season Feeding Habitat affected by construction of the railway has been reestablished using plants from a nursery set up prior to the construction.

   Adrail, with assistance from Greening Australia and the Kybrook Farm community at Pine Creek, have completed the required rehabilitation on the site at Yinberrie Hills.

The railway will have no impact on the heritage values of any declared heritage site; however, certificates have been obtained where the railway passes close to three declared heritage sites on the route of the old North Australian Railway line.

- Funding. The government's funding approach to the project was to provide an up front payment to ensure the railway is commercially viable and then let the private sector take over and bear the construction and the operating risks.

The Austral Asia Railway Corporation was established in 1997 by the South Australian and the North Territory governments after several failed attempts to have railway fully funded by the commonwealth government or a private company. Once government support had been affirmed, the corporation took the project to the market. In 1999, the Asia Pacific Transport (APT) Consortium was selected as the preferred tenderer and negotiations began on contractual details. In October 1999, government funding was finalized, with the Northern Territory providing $A 165 million, the South Australian Government $A 150 million, and the commonwealth $A 165 million. In January 2001, another $A 79 million in stand-by funding was provided by the three governments on commercial terms.

The model of BOOT (build, own, operate, transfer) was chosen and the ownership period set to 50 years – making it so affordable that 30 tenders were received from 60 national and international companies submitting expressions of interests.

- Design. High speed trains, particularly for passenger service, are very effective for moving large numbers of passengers in congested, densely populated areas, but require a wider corridor than conventional systems. In addition, electrification is generally feasible only in cities or heavily populated rural areas, while the need to connect older rail lines designed for slower trains cannot accommodate high speed lines without extensive upgrading.

The design chosen allows freight trains to travel at a maximum of 115 kph, although they operate most economically at 90 kph. Each train will be able to handle 250 double stacked containers, will be 1600 meters long, and will be powered by 4000 hp locomotives. Initially, there will be one train in each direction only. Still an upgrade will be needed for the older part of the rail.

- Subcontractors. APT established two companies – Adrail and FreightLink Pty – to operate as the main subcontractors for the project. Organizationally, the project was divided between many subcontractors and suppliers mostly according to their expertise and location so if one supplier failed for any reason another could take his place. Difficulties may still arise from suppliers such as Whyalla who is the sole source of steel rails, but precautions were taken to minimize them. In the case of Whyalla, payment was made in advance allowing it to pay it's big suppliers in advance

Some suppliers such as Austrak built special factories for this project (the sleeper factories in Katherine and Tennant Creek) and ballast quarries were also built in several locations near the rail's corridor. Above all, a tight but feasible schedule was set for each subproject.

- Raw material. To lower the transportation costs and to keep to schedule, special factories were built for the project in several nearby locations (Katherine's and Tennant Creek's sleeper factories and ballast quarries). Moreover, additional ballast site were identified and built along side the rail's corridor. For transshipment purposes, a logistics centre was built in Roe Creek – about 20 km south of Alice Springs, where the materials sent from south were concentrated and shipped north.

- High maintenance costs. To reduce the maintenance costs, the rail was constructed using a continuous weld line process so there are no joints to maintain. The strength and the quality of the welds are sufficient to hold the tracks together and prevent expansion or shrinkage of the steel. The cement sleepers are stronger and long lasting in comparison to those constructed from wood. The rails are held to the sleepers by heavy-duty spring clips, which prevent the rail from moving along the track. The weight of the sleepers and the friction of the ballast prevent any movement.

- Global recovery. Cost and revenue calculations were done using today's economic data and market forecasts. The company expects the rail to create new opportunities and thus enlarge its transportation capacity.

    Since the start of the 2001 global recession, the eastern markets (which are the main clients of the Darwin Port) have been growing rapidly. They have one of the lowest paid workforces in the world so as recovery takes hold, these markets will improve along with the economic outlook for the project.

(j) Based on the September 25th 2003 report, the track laying component of the project was completed much sooner than planned without any cost overruns. The entire infrastructure was built on schedule and the rail is ready to be used earlier than expected. At the end of June 2003, the company met its last financial commitment.

Looking at the benefits gained so far, the project has all the earmarks of a success:

- 1500 direct jobs and training opportunities were created (at peak) during construction and many more as a result of flow-on efforts to service and supply outlying areas

- Over $A 1 billion worth of contracts have been let to Northern Territory and South Australian companies

- Strong relationships have been built with local indigenous people, and major environmental and preservation activities have been carried out

- A new trade route (to Asia) has been built between the 500 million people to the north and the economic heartlands of south-eastern Australia

- Cheaper freight and competitive freight options now exist for the growing industrial base in the Northern Territory, and another option exists for cattle movements

- There has been a major boost to regional development and improved support for both the growing agribusiness in the Northern Territory and for South Australian food and wine exports.

- Cheaper transportation options have lent greater support to mineral exploration along the rail corridor.

- The new rail line has enhanced defense readiness by providing increased transportation options for troops and equipment.

(k) Of the $A 1.3 billion spent on the project, over 1.079 billion was awarded to industries in the Northern Territory and South Australia according to the contract documents. APT was required to allocate at least 75% of its budget to firms based in these regions. This was agreeable because its primary expertise is in railway operations. As a result, virtually all of the infrastructure associated with the project, such as buildings, fueling stations, carts, the port, quarries, and sleepers, was outsourced. This led to significant cost savings.

(l) Lessons learned

- Good planning is essential – a well-crafted plan pays off tenfold, providing solutions to problems before they arise

- Outsourcing may allow for better use of existing resources and lead to improved quality

- A well-designed project management process and good information flow are the keys to success

2.2   The solution is based on the information in the following article.

> E. A. Stohr and J. L. Zhao, "Workflow Automation: Overview and Research Issues," *Information Systems Frontiers*, Vol 3, No 3, pp 281-296 (2001).

(a) Advantages of workflow systems. In general, workflow systems can help businesses reduce costs and streamline operations. By using the correct process modeling technique and by defining detailed routing and processing requirements for the workflow, automation of the work process is enabled. As a result, human mistakes are minimized, work hours are saved, and operations flow smoothly.

- Workforce systems provides the following benefits:
  - i.   Simulation, prototyping and piloting – some systems have these options to allow testing before production begins
  - ii. Improved efficiency – mostly through automation of business processes and work lists
  - iii. Improved customer service – through consistency in the processes
  - iv. Improved/increased information flow – each step of the workflow identifies the required documentation and documentation routing, and provides limited access for remote customers, suppliers, collaborators, or staff to this information
  - v.   Improved process control – helps management to better understand processes and improve the quality of outcomes
  - vi. Flexibility – software control over processes enables the redesign of workflow as business needs change, thus creating opportunities for organizational change
  - vii. Business process improvement – through focus on business processes

(b) To be able to use a workflow management system in a project the following conditions must be present.

- The entire project has to be fully understood and mapped into processes.
- All processes involving human decision making have to be defined.
- The information on which the decision rules are built must be accurate and reliable.
- The project scope has to be divided into processes and each of these has to be well defined; i.e.,
  - i.   Each action and resource involved must be identified and the information flows defined
  - ii. Decision making rules have to be built including 'go'/ 'no go' for each step; exceptions should be noted
  - iii. The start and end of each process must be clearly specified.

(c) Of the nine process knowledge areas defined in the PMBOK, the oned best suited for workflow systems are in the procurement area. Purchasing functions tend to be project independent so the same process can be used repeatedly for different projects.

(d) The main problem in using a workflow system in a project is its dynamic, stochastic, one-time nature. Automated systems are designed to work in a static environment with permanent well-structured processes where the input data rarely change. In a dynamic, stochastic environment, the rigidity introduced by a workflow system may hurt the flexibility needed in the project environment while at the same time reducing the effectiveness of the workflow system. The problem is exacerbated by the fact that projects are, by definition, different from each.

2.3   Answers are based on information obtained from the following web sites:

- http://www.dist.maricopa.edu/users/bleed/learn.htm
- http://www.infed.org/thinkers/senge.htm
- http://websites.quincy.edu/~chasemi/learn.htm
- http://www.infed.org/biblio/learning-organization.htm
- http://www.skyrme.com/insights/3lrnorg.htm

(a) The "learning organization" is the label being used for an integration of a set of ideas that have emerged from organizational research and practice over the past three or four decades on ways of arranging work to met the often-conflicting demands of organizational objectives and individual job satisfaction. The learning organization is, in many ways, a natural evolution of older participatory management themes of the 1970s with recent emphasis on empowerment and self-managed work teams. It is not so much characterized by its altered structure (flatter and less hierarchal) and team emphasis, but by the transformation of the relationship of the organization to the individual and increased capacity for adaptation and change.

The previous overriding concern for control (e.g., motivate others, organize work for others, set goals for others) is replaced by a concern for learning by all organizational members on behalf of the organization. Learning about technical things and their relationship to the external environment is greatly valued, as is learning about organizational processes. A learning organization expects its members to " . . . act as agents, responding to changes in the internal and external environment of the organization by detecting and correcting errors in organizational theory-in-use, and embedding the results of their inquiry in private images and shared maps of organization." [C. Argyris and D. Schön, *Organizational learning II: Theory, Method and Practice*, Addison Wesley, Reading, MA (1996)].

(b) Peter Senge's 1990 book,
> *The Fifth Discipline. The Art and Practice of the Learning Organization*
> Random House, London

describes the five elements that make a learning organization:

1. Personal mastery: Learning to expand our personal capacity to create results we most desire, and creating an organizational environment which encourages all its members to develop themselves toward goals and purposes they choose.

2. Mental models: Reflecting upon, continually clarifying, and improving our internal pictures of the world, and seeing how they shape our actions and decisions.

3. Shared vision: Building a sense of commitment in a group by developing shared images of the future we seek to create as well as the principles and guiding practices by which we hope to get there.

4. Team learning: Transforming conversational and collective thinking skills so that groups of people can reliably develop intelligence and ability greater than the sum of individual members' talents.

5. Systems thinking: A way of thinking about and a language for describing and understanding forces and interrelationships that shape the behavior of systems. This discipline helps us see how to change systems more effectively and to act more in tune with the larger processes of the natural and economic world.

(c) The learning organization has the following advantages:

- It creates superior performance and quality – Because the organization is constantly learning and improving, its processes and products are also being constantly improved.

- It creates a competitive advantage – By improved processes and by achieving expertise the organization in able to make better products using more effective and cheaper processes (in comparison to past products and to the competition).

- It creates an energized, committed workforce – The workers are committed to the goals of the organization since they are involved in setting and achieving them. They are full participants in the learning process, and their success in becoming experts in their fields will encourage the organization to use their skills and promote them.

- It creates organizational changes – A learning organization better adjusts to change and is able to make them faster and more effectively when the environment dictates.

(d) To promote a learning organization in the project environment an organization has to identify and encourage professionalism on the part of its project managers. All workers should be rewarded for performance and encouraged to think and initiate process improvement. Progress must be documented but also mistakes. Information should be maintained within the organization for future use when best practices are identified (organizational memory). Performance has to be measured and documented as well.

An information system should be established enabling workers to enter the existing documentation and knowledge base of the organization and to communicate with fellow workers in order to exchange thoughts and information.

CHAPTER

3. ENGINEERING ECONOMIC ANALYSIS

3.1

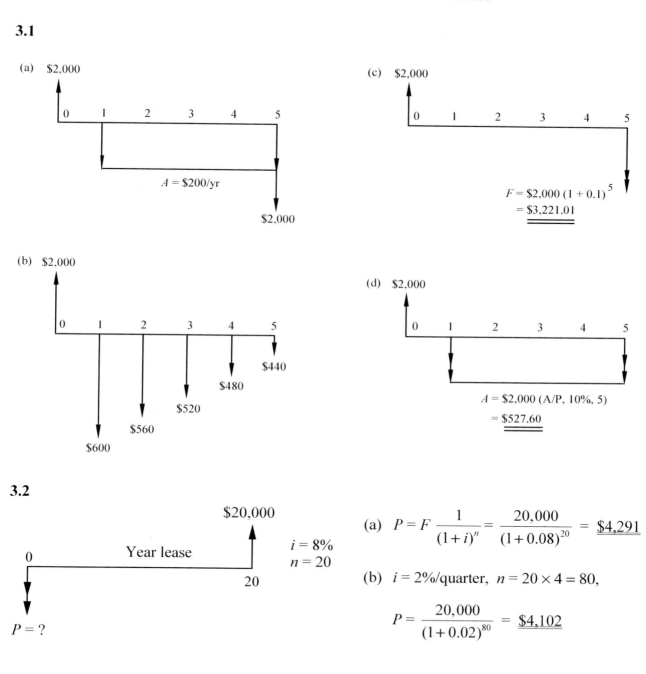

(a) $2,000

$A = \$200/\text{yr}$

$2,000

(b) $2,000

$440

$480

$520

$560

$600

(c) $2,000

$F = \$2,000 \, (1 + 0.1)^5$
$= \$3,221.01$

(d) $2,000

$A = \$2,000 \, (A/P, 10\%, 5)$
$= \$527.60$

3.2

$20,000

Year lease

$i = 8\%$
$n = 20$

20

$P = ?$

(a) $P = F \dfrac{1}{(1+i)^n} = \dfrac{20{,}000}{(1+0.08)^{20}} = \underline{\$4{,}291}$

(b) $i = 2\%/\text{quarter}, \quad n = 20 \times 4 = 80,$

$P = \dfrac{20{,}000}{(1+0.02)^{80}} = \underline{\$4{,}102}$

– 23 –

3.3   (a) $10,000 now

(b)

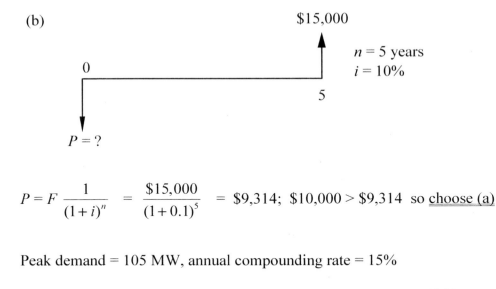

$15,000

$n = 5$ years
$i = 10\%$

$P = ?$

$$P = F \frac{1}{(1+i)^n} = \frac{\$15,000}{(1+0.1)^5} = \$9,314; \quad \$10,000 > \$9,314 \text{ so } \underline{\text{choose (a)}}$$

3.4   Peak demand = 105 MW, annual compounding rate = 15%

(a) $240 = 105(1 + 0.15)^n$ so

$n = \underline{5.91 \text{ years}}$

(b) $F = 105 (1 + 0.15)^{10.91}$

$F = 432.4$ (total demand)
$- \underline{240.0}$ (present capacity)
242.4 (MW needed)

Roughly $\underline{243 \text{ MW}}$ of capacity are needed.

3.5   (a) $F = P(1 + i)^n$; $F = 89,920$; $P = 49,050$; $n = 10$; $i = \left(\dfrac{F}{P}\right)^{1/n} - 1 = \underline{6.25\%}$

(b) $F = 80,300$; $P = 49,050$; $i = 6.25\%$

$$n = \frac{\ln(F/P)}{\ln(1+i)} = \underline{8.13 \text{ years}} \Rightarrow 10 - 8.13 = \underline{1.87 \text{ years ago}}$$

(c) $n = 10$; $i = 6.25\%$; P $= 803$; $F = 803 (1.0625)^{10} = 1,472$; $F - P = \underline{669 \text{ acres}}$

3.6   (a) $F = 240 \ (F/A, 9\%, 40) = \$81,100$

(b) $F = 240 \ (F/A, 12\%, 40) = \$184,100$

(c) $n = (4)(40) = 160$; $i = \dfrac{12}{4} = 3$; $F = 60(F/A, 3\%, 160) = \$224,500$

(d) $i_{\text{eff}} = (1.03)^4 - 1 = 12.55\% = 12.6\%$

3.7

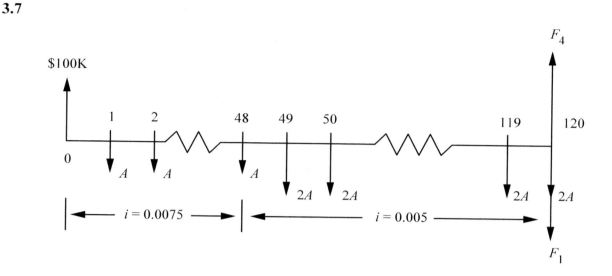

$F_1 = P(F/P, 1\%, 120) = \$330{,}039; \quad F_2 = A \, (F/A, 0.75\%, 48) \, (F/P, 0.5\%, 72) = A(82.372)$

$F_3 = 2A \, (F/A, 0.5\%, 72) = A(172.818); \quad F_4 = F_2 + F_3 = A(255.19); \quad F_4 = F_1$

$A(255.19) = 330{,}039 \;\rightarrow\; \underline{A = \$1{,}293}$

3.8   (a)

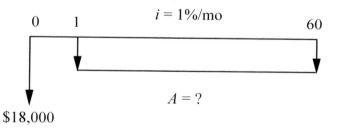

$P = 20{,}000(1 - 0.10) = 18{,}000; \quad A = P(A/P, 1\%, 60) = 18{,}000(0.0222) = \underline{\$400.40/\text{mo}}$

(b) $i_{\text{eff}} = (1.01)^{12} - 1 = \underline{12.68\%}$

3.9   Renovation cost = \$100,000; Benefit = $\left(2,000\frac{hr}{yr}\right)\left(10\frac{yd^3}{hr}\right)\left(\frac{\$1}{yd^3}\right)$ = \$20,000 / yr

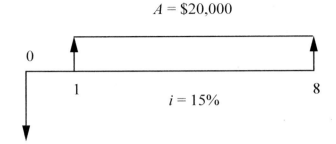

$A = \$20,000$

$i = 15\%$

PW = −100,000 + 20,000(*P/A*, 15%, 8) = −100,000 + 20,000(4.48732) = −\$10,253

The fact that PW is negative implies that the ROR < 15% so the investment does not meet the company's objective.

3.10   (a) $A = P(A/P, i\%, n) = \$50,000(A/P, 8\%, 10) = \$50,000(0.14903) = \underline{\$7,451.5}$

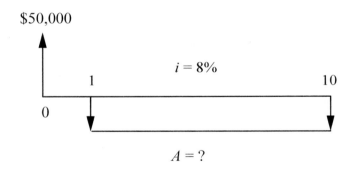

$\$50,000$

$i = 8\%$

$A = ?$

(b)   Charge = $\dfrac{7,451.5 \ \$/yr}{2,000 \ hr/yr}$ = \$3.73/hr

(c)

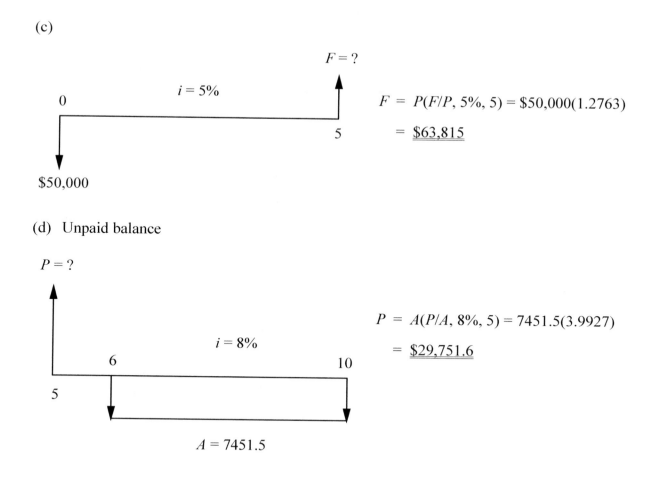

$F = P(F/P, 5\%, 5) = \$50,000(1.2763)$

$\qquad = \underline{\$63,815}$

(d) Unpaid balance

$P = A(P/A, 8\%, 5) = 7451.5(3.9927)$

$\qquad = \underline{\$29,751.6}$

3.11 $F_1 = 2(10^6)\ (F/P, 8\%, 2) = P_2 = \$2,332,800$

$A = P_2\ (A/P, 8\%, 20) = 2,332,800\ (0.10185) = 237,595.7$

Let Y be the charge per vehicle. Then $(3,650,000\ \text{vehicles/yr}) \times Y = \$237,595.7/\text{yr}$

$\rightarrow Y = \underline{\$0.065/\text{vehicle}}$

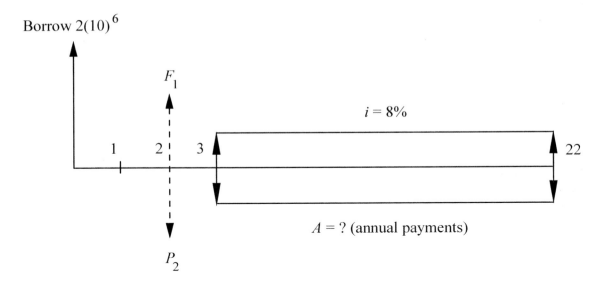

3.12

Year	Cash flow		Transformed cash flow
0	−$15,000		−$15,000
1	+10,000 − 1,142.86/1.12 = 8,980		+8,980
2	+6,000 − 8,000/1.12 = −1,142.86		0
3	−8,000		0
4	+4,000		+4,000
5	+4,000		+4,000
6	+4,000		+4,000

Year	Transformed cash flow	PW at 10%	PW at 12%
0	−$15,000	−$15,000	−$15,000
1	+8,980	+8,164	+8,018
2	0	0	0
3	0	0	0
4	+4,000	+2,372	+2,542
5	+4,000	+2,484	+2,270
6	+4,000	+2,258	+2,026
		+638	−144

$$\text{Rate of return} = 10\% + 2\% \left(\frac{638}{638 + 144} \right) = \underline{11.6\%}$$

3.13

Plan	Cost of improvements and land	Net annual income	Salvage value	Computed rate of return	Decision
A	$145,000	$23,300	$70,000	15%	
B	300,000	44,300	70,000	12.9%	
C	100,000	10,000	70,000	9%	Fails to meet the 10% criterion ==> **Reject**
D	200,000	27,500	70,000	12%	

Rank the three remaining projects in order of cost and examine each investment increment.

Plan D rather than Plan A

Δ Investment	Δ Annual Income	Δ Salvage Value
$55,000	$4,200	$0

Plan D rather than Plan A

Δ Investment	Δ Annual Income	Δ Salvage Value
$55,000	$4,200	$0

$$\$55,000 = \$4,200\ (P/A,\ i\%,\ 15);\quad (P/A,\ i\%,\ 15) = \frac{55,000}{4,200} = 13.1$$

From the interest tables, we find that $i = 1\frac{3}{4}\%$

This is an unacceptable increment of investment. **Reject D and retain A.**

Plan B rather than Plan A

Δ Investment	Δ Annual Income	Δ Salvage Value
$155,000	$21,000	$0

$$\$155,000 = \$21,000\ (P/A,\ i\%,\ 15);\quad (P/A,\ i\%,\ 15) = \frac{155,000}{21,200} = 7.38$$

From the interest tables: $i = 10.5\%$

This is an acceptable increment of investment. **Reject A and accept B.**

Conclusion: **Select Plan B.** The exercise shows that the project with the highest ROR is not always the best.

3.14

Year	Plan A cash flow	Plan B cash flow	Plan B rather than Plan A	Plan C cash flow	Plan C rather than Plan B
0	−10,000	−15,000	−5,000	−20,000	−5,000
1-10	+1,625	+1,625	0	+1,890	+265
10	−10,000	0	+10,000	0	0
11-20	+1,625	+1,625	0	+1,890	+265
rate of return	10%*	8.8%	7.2%**	7%	0.6%***

*The computation may be made for a 10-year period:

$$10,000 = 1,625 \ (P/A, i, 10) \ \rightarrow \ \underline{i = 10\%}$$

The second 10-year period has the same rate of return.

**The computation is:

$$5,000 = 10,000(P/F, i, 10) \ \text{ so } \ (P/F, i, 10) = \frac{5,000}{10,000} = 0.5 \ \rightarrow \ \underline{i = 7.2\%}$$

***Here the computation is:

$$5,000 = 265(P/A, i, 20) \ \rightarrow \ \underline{i = 0.6\%}$$

3.15 *Incremental Rate-of-Return Solution*

	A	B	C	D	C–D	B–C	A–C
					\multicolumn{3}{}{Increment}		
Cost	1,000	800	600	500	100	200	400
Uniform annual benefit	122	120	97	122	−25	23	25
Salvage value	750	500	500	0	500	0	250
Computed incremental rate of return					10%	<0%	−18%

The C-D increment is desirable.   Reject D and retain C
The B-C increment is undesirable.   Reject B and retain C
The A-C increment is undesirable.   Reject A and retain C

Select alternative C

Net Present Worth Solution

Net present worth = uniform annual benefit $(P/A, 8\%, 8)$ + salvage value $(P/F, 8\%, 8)$
− initial cost

$$NPW_A = 122\,(5.747) + 750\,(0.5403) - 1000 = +106.36$$
$$NPW_B = 120\,(5.747) + 500\,(0.5403) - 800 = +159.79$$
$$NPW_C = 97\,(5.747) + 500\,(0.5403) - 600 = +227.61$$
$$NPW_D = 122\,(5.747) - 500 = +201.13$$

<u>Select alternative C</u>

3.16 Costs = benefits at end of year 8 → payback period = <u>8 yrs</u>

3.17 Because both motors have the same annual maintenance cost, it may be ignored in the computations. Here, however, we will include it. For a 20-year planning horizon, we have:

Teledyne

$$EUAC_T = 7,000\,(A/P, 10\%, 20) + 300 + \frac{(200hp)(0.746Kw/hp)(\$0.072/Kwhr)}{0.89eff}\,(Hours)$$
$$= 7,000\,(0.1175) + 300 + 12.07\,(Hours) = 1,122.5 + 12.07 \times hours$$

Allison

$$EUAC_A = 6,000\,(A/P, 10\%, 20) + 300 + \frac{(200hp)(0.746Kw/hp)(\$0.072/Kwhr)}{0.85eff}\,(Hours)$$
$$= 705 + 300 + 12.64 \times Hours$$

Set $EUAC_A = EUAC_T$: $\quad 1,005 + 12.64 \times Hours = 1,122.50 + 12.07 \times Hours$

Solving this equation gives the minimum number of hours the Teledyne, with its smaller power cost, must be used.

$$Hours = \frac{1122.5 - 1005}{12.64 - 12.07} = \frac{117.50}{0.57} \rightarrow \underline{206\ Hours}$$

3.18 Income = \$800/mo; Expenses = \$600/yr; Net = \$9,000/yr

SOYD depreciation: $N = 20$ $\quad SUM = \frac{N}{2} \times (N+1) = 210$

First year depreciation $= \frac{20}{210} \times (93,000 - 9,000) = \$8,000$

Declining gradient $= \frac{1}{210} \times (93,000 - 9,000) = \$400$

Year	Before tax cash flow	SOYD depreciation	Taxable income	38% Income taxes	After-tax cash flow
0	−93,000				−93,000
1	+9,000	8,000	1,000	−380	+8,620
2	+9,000	7,600	1,400	−532	+8,468
3	+9,000	7,200	1,800	−684	+8,316
.	.	.	.	.	$G = -152$
.	.	.	.	.	.
.	.	.	.	.	.

Assumption (a)

20	+9,000	400	8,600	−3,268	+5,732
	+9,000 lot + bldg		0		+9,000

Assumption (b)

20	+9000	400	8,600	−3,268	+5,732
	+100,000 lot + bldg		91,000*	−34,580**	+65,420

*Capital gains = selling price − (cost − deprec.) = 100,000 − (93,000 − 84,000) = 91,000

**Capital gains taxed at 38%

After-tax rate of return, based on assumption (a) PW of benefit − PW of cost = 0

$8620(P/A, i, 20) - 152(P/G, i, 20) + 9,000(P/F, i, 20) - 93,000 = 0$

Try i = 4.5%

$8,620(13,008) - 152 (P/G, 4.5\%, 20) + 9,000 (0.4146) - 93,000 = +6,934$

Try i = 6%

$8,620(11.470) - 152 (87.23) + 9,000 (0.3118) - 93,000 = -4,581$

$$i = 4.5\% + 1.5\% \frac{6,934}{4,581 + 6,934} = \underline{5.4\%}$$

3.19   Parts (a) & (b)

Year	Before-tax cash flow	Straight line depreciation	Taxable income	40% income taxes	After-tax cash flow
0	−20,000				−20,000
1-8	+5,000	2,500	2,500	−1,000	+4,000
	Totals:	20,000	20,000	−8,000	

(a) Before-tax rate of return

$$20,000 = 5,000(P/A, i, 8): \quad (P/A, i, 8) = \frac{20,000}{5,000} = 4 \quad \rightarrow \quad i = \underline{18.6\%}$$

(b) After-tax rate of return

$$20,000 = 4,000(P/A, i, 8): \quad (P/A, i, 8) = \frac{20,000}{4,000} = 5 \rightarrow i = \underline{11.8\%}$$

(c)

Year	Before-tax cash flow	Straight line depreciation	Taxable income	40% income taxes	After-tax cash flow
0	−20,000				−20,000
1-8	+5,000	1,000	4,000	−1,600	+3,400
9-20	0	1,000	−1,000	+400	+400
Totals:		20,000	20,000	−8,000	

Note that the changed depreciable life does not change *total depreciation, total taxable income*, or *total income taxes*; however, it does change the timing of these items.

(c) After-tax rate of return; PW of benefits − PW of cost = 0

$$400(P/A, i, 20) + 3,000 (P/A, i, 8) - 20,000 = 0$$

For $i = 9\%$: $400(9,129) + 3000(5.535) - 20,000 = +256.60$
For $i = 10\%$: $400(8.514) + 3000(5.535) - 20,000 = -589.40$

Interpolation gives $i \cong \underline{9.3\%}$

3.20   *EUAC of Capital Recovery*

In this situation $P = S = \$15,000$, so EUAC of capital recovery = $\$15,000 (0.15) = \$2,250$ for all useful lives.

EUAC of Maintenance

For a 1-year useful life, we have

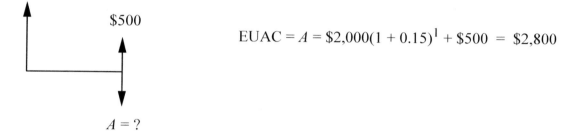

$$\text{EUAC} = A = \$2,000(1 + 0.15)^1 + \$500 = \$2,800$$

For a 2-year useful life, we have

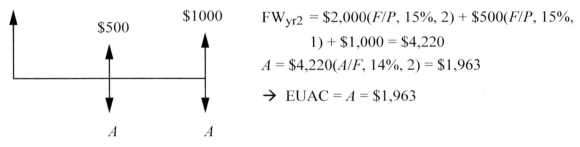

$$FW_{yr2} = \$2,000(F/P, 15\%, 2) + \$500(F/P, 15\%, 1) + \$1,000 = \$4,220$$

$$A = \$4,220(A/F, 14\%, 2) = \$1,963$$

$$\rightarrow EUAC = A = \$1,963$$

For a 3-year useful life,

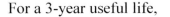

$$FW_{yr3} = \$2,000(F/P, 15\%, 3) + \$500(F/P, 15\%, 2) + \$1,000(F/P, 15\%, 1) + \$1,500$$

$$= \$6,353$$

$$A = \$6,353 \, (A/F, 15\%, 3) = \$1,829 \rightarrow EUAC = A = \$1,829$$

For a 4-year useful life,

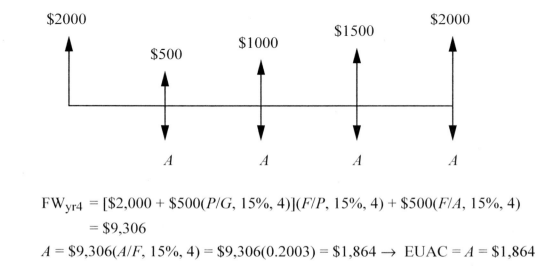

$$FW_{yr4} = [\$2,000 + \$500(P/G, 15\%, 4)](F/P, 15\%, 4) + \$500(F/A, 15\%, 4)$$

$$= \$9,306$$

$$A = \$9,306(A/F, 15\%, 4) = \$9,306(0.2003) = \$1,864 \rightarrow EUAC = A = \$1,864$$

(a) Total EUAC = $2,250 + EUAC of maintenance; therefore, to minimize Total EUAC, choose the alternative with minimum EUAC of maintenance.

<u>Economic life = 3 years</u>

(b) The stainless steel tank will always be compared with the best available replacement (the challenger). If the challenger is superior, then the defender tank probably will be replaced. It will cost a substantial amount of money to remove the existing tank from the plant, sell it to someone else, and then buy and install another one. As a practical matter, it seems unlikely that this will be economical.

3.21 (a) Before-tax analysis

Year	New machine before-tax cash flow	Existing machine before-tax cash flow	New machine rather than existing machine before-tax cash flow
0	–3,700	–1,000	–2,700
1	+900	0	+900
2	+900	0	+900
3	+900	0	+900
4	+900	0	+900

Compute rate of return; PW of cost = PW of Benefits

$$2,700 = 900(P/A, i, 4) \rightarrow (P/A, i, 4) = \frac{2,700}{900} = 3.0; \text{ ROR} \rightarrow \underline{i = 12.6\%}$$

(b) After-tax analysis

New machine

Year	Before-tax cash flow	SOYD depreciation	Taxable income	40% income taxes	After-tax cash flow
0	–3,700				–3,700
1	+900	1,480	–580	+232	+1,132
2	+900	1,110	–210	+84	+984
3	+900	740	+160	–64	+836
4	+900	370	+530	–212	+688

SOYD depreciation: Sum $= \frac{4}{2}(5) = 10$; 1st yr. SOYD $= \frac{4}{10}(3,700 - 0) = 1480$

Annual decline $= \frac{1}{10}(3,700 - 0) = 370$

Existing machine

Year	Before-tax cash flow	Straight line depreciation	Taxable income	40% income tax	After-tax cash flow
0	−1,000		1,000*	−400**	−1,400
1	0	500	−500	+200	+200
2	0	500	−500	+200	+200
3	0	500	−500	+200	+200
4	0	500	−500	+200	+200

* Long-term capital loss foregone by keeping machine
  = $2,000 book value − $1,000 selling price = $1,000 capital loss

** The $1,000 long-term capital loss foregone would have offset $1,000 of long-term capital gains elsewhere in the firm. The result is a tax saving of 40%($1,000) = $400.

New machine rather than existing one

Year	New tool after-tax cash flow	Existing tool after-tax cash flow	New − existing after-tax cash flow	PW @ 10%	PW @ 12%
0	−3,700	−1,400	−2,300	−2,300	−2,300
1	+1,132	+200	932	847	832
2	+984	+200	784	648	625
3	+836	+200	636	478	453
4	+688	+200	488	333	310
			+540	+6	-80

Δ after-tax rate of return = <u>10.14%</u>

3.22 Before tax rate of return = 20%; n = 10 years

PC_A = $120,000 + $20,000(P/A, 20%, 10) − $20,000(P/F, 20%, 10) = <u>$200,619</u>

AC_A = <u>$47,852</u>

PC_B = $150,000 + $15,000(P/A, 20%, 10) − $30,000(P/F, 20%, 10) = <u>$208,042</u>

AC_B = <u>$49,623</u>

Conclusion: Choose alternative A

Alternative solution

PW_{B-A} = −$30,000 + $5,000(P/A, 20%, 10) + $10,000(P/A, 20%, 10)

= −$30,000 + $5,000(4.1925) + $10,000(0.1615) = −$7,423

Because PW_{B-A} is negative, choose alternative A

3.23 (a) P/G $=$ $(A/G)(P/A)$

PC_A $=$ $\$100,000 + \$5,000(P/A, 20\%, 20) + \$1,000(P/G, 20\%, 20)$

$+ \$10,000(A/F, 20\%, 5)(P/A, 20\%, 20) - \$20,000\ (P/F, 20\%, 20)$

$= \$100,000 + \$5,000(4.8696) + \$1,000(21.739)$

$+ \$10,000(0.1344)(4.8696) - \$20,000(0.261) = \underline{\$152,110}$

PC_B $=$ $\$40,000 + \$40,000(P/F, 20\%, 10) + \$10,000(P/A, 20\%, 20)$

$+ \$2,000\ (P/G, 20\%, 10) + \$2,000(P/G, 20\%, 10)(P/F, 20\%, 10)$

$- \$10,000(P/F, 20\%, 10) - \$10,000(P/F, 20\%, 20) = \underline{\$123,217}$

Conclusion: Choose alternative B

(b) AC_A $=$ $\$100,000(A/P, 20\%, 20) + \$5,000 + \$1,000(A/G, 20\%, 20)$

$+ \$10,000\ (A/F, 20\%, 5) - \$20,000(A/F, 20\%, 20) = \underline{\$31,244}$

AC_B $=$ $\$40,000(A/P, 20\%, 10) + \$10,000 + \$2,000(A/G, 20\%, 10)$

$- \$10,000(A/F, 20\%, 10) = \underline{\$25,303}$

Conclusion: Choose alternative B

3.24 (a) The investor will require $i' = 0.12 + 0.08 + (0.12)(0.08) = 0.2096 \rightarrow 20.96\%$

(b) If the labor cost is \$15 an hour today and the inflation rate is 6%, the labor cost is expected to be to $\$15(1.06)^3 = \$17.87$

3.25 The first step is to determine the MARR without inflation. For $f = 7\%$ and $i' = 12\%$, the uninflated interest rate is

$$i = (i' - f)/(1 + f) = 0.0467 \text{ or } 4.67\%$$

We now do the analysis with i.

$$x = 500(P/A, i, 5) + 600(P/G, i, 5) \text{ or } x = \underline{\$7188.65}$$

Alternatively, inflate dollars and use i' for the present worth analysis.

$x = 500(F/P, f, 1)(P/F, i', 1) + 1100(F/P, f, 2)(P/F, i', 2) + 1700(F/P, f, 3)(P/F, i', 3) +$

$2300(F/P, f, 4)(P/F, i', 4) + 2900(F/P, f, 5)(P/F, i', 5) = \underline{\$7188.65}$

3.26 (a) The general rate of inflation is 6% and future cash flows are expected to increase with inflation. The cash flows in actual dollars are:

Time	0	1	2	3	4	5
Cash flow	−2000	212	449	715	1010	1338

$CF(0) = -2000$, $CF(1) = 200 \times 1.06 = 212.00$, $CF(2) = 400 \times 1.06^2 = 449$,

$CF(3) = 600 \times 1.06^3 = 715$, $CF(4) = 800 \times 1.06^4 = 1010$, $CF(5) = 1000 \times 1.06^5 = 1338$

(b) Your MARR without considering inflation is 10%. Because all cash flows increase with inflation, it is sufficient to use the MARR without inflation. Now find the NPV.

$NPV = -2000 + 200(P/A, 0.1, 5) + 200(P/G, 0.1, 5)$

$NPV = -2000 + 200 \times 3.791 + 200 \times 6.862 = -2000 + 758.2 + 1372.4 = 130.6$

Given that the NPV > 0, **accept** the investment.

3.27 For an after tax analysis you must compute the depreciation first.

$SOYD = 1 + 2 + 3 + 4 + 5 = 15$. $D_1 = 5 \times 2000/15 = 666$, $D_2 = 4 \times 2000/15 = 533$,

$D_3 = 3 \times 2000/15 = 400$, $D_4 = 2 \times 2000/15 = 266$, $D_5 = 2000/15 = 133$

Solution 1: The analysis can be done with year-n cash flows using the interest rate

$u = 0.1 + 0.06 + 0.1 \times 0.06 = 0.16 + 0.006 = 0.166$ or 16.6%.

For year 1: Tax $= (212 - 666) \times 0.4 = -454 \times 0.4 = -181.6$, ATCF $= 212 - (-181.6) = 393.6$

For year 2: Tax $= (449 - 533) \times 0.4 = -33.6$, ATCF $= 449 - (-33.6) = 482.6$

For year 3: Tax $= (715 - 400) \times 0.4 = 126$, ATCF $= 715 - 126 = 589$

For year 4: Tax $= (1010 - 266) \times 0.4 = 297.6$, ATCF $= 1010 - 297.6 = 712.4$

For year 5: Tax $= (1338 - 133) \times 0.4 = 1205 \times 0.4 = 482.0$, ATCF $= 1338 - 482.0 = 856$

Time	0	1	2	3	4	5
AFCF	−2000	393.6	482.6	589	712.4	856

Now find NPV at 16.6%.

Solution 2: The analysis is easier, however, if it is done with year-0 cash flows and an interest rate of 10%. This requires that the depreciation payments first be deflated.

Deflating the depreciation: $D_1 = 666.000/1.06 = 628.3$, $D_2 = 533/1.06^2 = 474.4$, $D_3 = 400/1.06^3 = 335.8$, $D_4 = 266/1.06^4 = 210.7$, $D_5 = 133.000/1.06^5 = 133/1.3382 = 99.4$

For year 1: Tax $= (200 - 628.3) \times 0.4 = -428.3 \times 0.4 = -171.3$, ATCF $= 200 - (-171.3)$
$= 371.3$

For year 2: Tax = $(400 - 474.4) \times 0.4 = -29.8$, ATCF = $400 - (-29.8) = 429.8$

For year 3: Tax = $(600 - 335.8) \times 0.4 = 105.7$, ATCF = $600 - 105.7 = 494.3$

For year 4: Tax = $(800 - 210.7) \times 0.4 = 235.7$, ATCF = $800 - 235.7 = 564.3$

For year 5: Tax = $(1000 - 99.4) \times 0.4 = 900.6 \times 0.4 = 360.2$, ATCF = $1000 - 360.2 = 639.8$

Time	0	1	2	3	4	5
AFCF	−2000	371	429.8	494.3	564.3	639.8

NPW = $371(P/F,10\%,1) + 429.8(P/F,10\%,2) + 494.3(P/F,10\%,3) + 564.3(P/F,10\%,4) +$
    $639.8(P/F,10\%,5) - 2000$

NPW = $371.3(0.9091) + 429.8(0.8264) + 494.3(0.7513) + 564.3(0.6830) + 639.8(0.6209) -$
    $2000 = -153.2$ ← **Reject**

3.28 (a) First find the cash flows from year 0 to year 8, and then compute the NPV at 8%.

Cash flow: Year 0 = −$5,000; Years 5 – 8 = +$2,500

NPV at 8% = $-\$5,000 + \$2,500(P/A, 0.08, 4)(P/F, 0.08, 4)$

$= -\$5,000 + (\$2,500)(3.312)(0.7350) = -\$5,000 + \$6,085.8 = \underline{\$1,085.8}$

→ Investment is *acceptable*.

(b) There are two ways to solve this problem. The first is to convert all cash flows to year-0 dollars and use $i = 8\%$. Deflating the $2,500 payments to constant (year-0) dollars.

Year	Year-0 $
5	$1958.82
6	1865.54
7	1776.7
8	1692.1

NPV at 8% $= -5,000 + 1958 \times 0.6806 + 1865.54 \times 0.6302 + 1776.7 \times 0.5835$
    $+ 1692.1 \times 0.5403$
    $= -\$5,000 + 1332.61 + 1175.66 + 1036.71 + 914.24 = \underline{-\$540.78}$

Alternatively, we could use the interest rate adjusted for inflation.

$i' = i + f + i \times f = 0.08 + 0.05 + 0.004 = 13.4\%$. Computing the NPV directly using the

formulas NPV = $-\$5,000 + \$2,500(P/A, 0.134, 4)(P/F, 0.134, 4) = -\$540.78$

→ Investment is *not acceptable.*

3.29 (a) Formula for investment without taxes and without inflation:

$$\text{NPV} = -\$10,000 + \$1,000(P/A, 0.2, 5) + 80(P/F, 0.2, 5)$$

(b) Formula for investment with taxes and without inflation:

$$\text{NPV} = \text{NPV} = -\$10,000 + \$1,400(P/A, 0.2, 5) + \$4,800(P/F, 0.2, 5)$$

The depreciation each year is $2,000. The taxable income is $1,000 – $2,000 = –$1,000.

The tax is –$400 so the after-tax cash flow is $1,000 – (–$400) = $1,400

The BV after 5 years is zero. The taxable income is $8,000. The tax is $3,200 so the after-tax salvage is $8,000 – $3,200 = $4,800.

(c) Formula for investment without taxes but with inflation:

Because everything is increasing at the inflation rate, we can use the original cash flows and 20%.

$$\text{NPV} = -\$10,000 + \$1,000(P/A, 0.2, 5) + 80(P/F, 0.2, 5)$$

The problem can also be done with inflated cash flows and interest rate $i' = 20\% + 10\% + (20\%)(10\%) = 32\%$.

(d) Formula for investment with taxes and with inflation:

We must express the ATCF in either actual $ or real $. Use 20% if using real $ or the 32% if using actual $.

ATCF in actual $

Straight line depreciation → $10,000/5 = $2,000

Year	BTCF (actual)	Deprec. (actual)	Taxable income (actual)	Tax	ATCF (actual)
0	-$10,000				-$10,000
1	1,100	$2,000	-$900	-$360	1,460
2	1,210	2,000	-790	-320	1,530
3	1,330	2,000	-670	-270	1,600
4	1,460	2,000	-540	-220	1,680
5	1,610	2,000	-390	-160	1,770
salvage =	$8,000(1.1)^5$ = 12,880		12,880	5,160	7,720

$$\text{NPW} = -\$10{,}000 + \$1{,}460(P/F, 32\%, 1) + \$1{,}530(P/F, 32\%, 2) + \$1{,}600(P/F, 32\%, 3)$$
$$+ \$1{,}680(P/F, 32\%, 4) + (\$1{,}770 + \$7{,}720)(P/F, 32\%, 5)$$
$$= -\$10{,}000 + \$1{,}460/(1.32)^1 + \$1{,}530/(1.32)^2 + \$1{,}600/(1.32)^3 + \$1{,}680/(1.32)^4$$
$$+ \$9{,}490/(1.32)^5$$
$$= -\$10{,}000 + \$1{,}106 + \$878 + \$696 + \$553 + \$2{,}368 = \underline{-\$4{,}399}$$

3.30 (a) You must compute the net annual cost (NAC) for each of the 3 years using an interest rate of 10%.

NAC 1 $= \$50{,}000(A/P, 0.1, 1) + \$10{,}000 = \$50{,}000 \times 1.1 + \$10000 = \$65{,}000$

NAC 2 $= \$50{,}000(A/P, 0.1, 2) + \$10{,}000 + \$30{,}000(A/G, 0.1, 2)$

$\quad = \$50{,}000 \times 0.5762 + \$10{,}000 + \$30{,}000 \times 0.476 = \$28{,}810 + \$10{,}000 + 14{,}280$

$\quad = \$53{,}090 \leftarrow$ **minimum**

NAC 3 $= \$50{,}000(A/P, 0.1, 3) + \$10{,}000 + \$30{,}000(A/G, 0.1, 3)$

$\quad = \$50{,}000 \times 0.4021 + \$10{,}000 + \$30{,}000 \times 0.937 = \$20{,}105 + 10{,}000 + \$28{,}110$

$\quad = \$58{,}215$

The economic life is **2 years**.

(b)

NAC 1 $= \$50{,}000(A/P, 0.1, 1) + \$10{,}000 - \$30{,}000(A/F, 0.1, 1) = \$50{,}000 \times 1.1 - \$20{,}000$

$\quad = \$35{,}000$

NAC 2 $= \$50{,}000(A/P, 0.1, 2) + \$10{,}000 - \$20{,}000(A/F, 0.1, 2)$

$\quad = \$50{,}000 \times 0.5762 + \$10{,}000 - \$20{,}000 \times 0.4762 = \$28{,}810 + \$10{,}000 - \$9{,}524$

$\quad = \$29{,}286 \leftarrow$ **minimum**

NAC 3 $= \$50{,}000(A/P, 0.1, 3) + 10000 = \$50{,}000 \times 0.4021 + \$10{,}000$

$\quad = \$20{,}105 + \$10{,}000 = \$30{,}105$

The economic life is **2 years**.

3.31 (a) Begin by computing the depreciation. For a 6-year tax life, the SYOD is $6 \times 7/2 = 21$.

The depreciation for the first 3 years is

> Year 1: $\$14,000 \times 6 / 21 = \$4,000$
> Year 2: $\$14,000 \times 5 / 21 = \$3,333$
> Year 3: $\$14,000 \times 4 / 21 = \$2,667$

The book value after 3 years is $\$14,000 - \$4,000 - \$3,333 - \$2,667 = \$4,000$

Selling the asset for $\$10,000$, results in a taxable gain of $\$6,000$. The tax is $\$2,400$, so the net receipts are <u>$\$7,600$</u>.

(b) First compute the economic life of the old machine.

NAC for 1 year $= (\$10,000 - \$6,000)(A/P, 0.1, 1) + \$6,000 \times 0.1 + \$1,000$

> $= \$4,000 \times 1.1 + \$600 + \$1000 = \$6,000$

The NAC for 2 years $= (\$10,000 - \$4,000)(A/P, 0.1, 2) + \$4,000 \times 0.1 + \$1,000$

> $= \$6,000 \times 0.5762 + \$400 + \$1,000 = \$3457.20 + 400 + \$1,000$

> $= \$4,857.20$ ← **minimum**

The NAC for 3 years $= (\$10,000)(A/P, 0.1, 3) = \$10,000 \times 0.4021 + \$1,000$

> $= \$4,021 + \$1,000 = \$5,021$.

The economic life of the old machine is 2 years. It's NAC at this life is less than that of the challenger. → *Keep the old machine.*

3.32 Machine A (*defender*):

Compute book value, BTCF and ATCF.

BV $= $ cost $-$ depreciation to date

> $= \$54,000 - (9/12)(\$54,000 - 0) = \$13,500$.

Long term capital gain if sold now $= \$30,000 - \$13,500 = \$16,500$

Net return if machine A is replaced $= \$30,000 - \$16,500 \times 0.4 = \$23,400$

Machine A annual depreciation $= (P - S)/N = (\$54,000 - 0)/12 = \$4,500$ for 3 more years.

Keep machine A for 12 more years:

Year	BTCF	Depr.	Taxable Income	Income tax	ATCF
0	−30,000				−23,400
1 - 3	−7,500	4,500	−12,000	−4,800	−2,700
4 - 12	−7,500	0	−7,500	−3,000	−4,500

After-tax net annual cost:

$$\text{NAC} = [\$23,400 - \$1,800(P/A,10\%,3)](A/P,10\%,12) + \$4,500$$

$$= [\$23,400 - \$1,800(2.487)][0.1468] + \$4,500 = \$7,278$$

The after tax cash flow in year 0 reflects the loss of income after capital gains tax from not selling machine A.

Machine B (*challenger*):

Annual depreciation = $(P - S)/N = (\$42,000 - 0)/12 = \$3,500$

Year	BTCF	Depr.	Taxable income	Income tax	ATCF
0	−42,000				−42,000
1 - 12	−5,000	3,500	−8,500	−3,400	−1,600

After-tax net annual cost:

$$\text{NAC} = \$42,000(A/P,10\%,12) + 1600 = \$7,766$$

Choose the alternative with smaller annual cost → **Keep Machine A**

3.33 The argument is that 50-50 gambles are easier to conceptualize and explain.

3.34 If special attitudes toward risk can be identified, they place restrictions on the shape of the preference curve. This means that curves can be obtained with fewer certainty equivalent assessments. The most dramatic example is risk neutrality. In this case, no other assessments are required.

3.35 $U(1,000) = 1.0, \ U(0) = 0, \ U(400) = 0.5$

$U(100) = 0.5U(400) + 0.5U(0) = 0.5 \times 0.5 + 0.5 \times 0 = 0.25$

3.36 $U(10M) = 1.0, \ U(-10M) = 0$

$U(-5M) = 0.5U(10M) + 0.5U(-10M) = 0.5 \times 1 + 0.5 \times 0 = 0.5$

$U(0) = 0.5U(10M) + 0.5U(-5M) = 0.5 \times 1 + 0.5 \times 0.5 = 0.75$

$U(5M) = 0.7U(10M) + 0.3U(0) = 0.7 \times 1 + 0.3 \times 0.75 = 0.925$

3.37

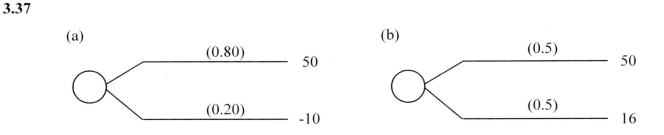

(a)

(b)

These are just two of the possible gambles with a certainty equivalent of 30. Any gamble with an expected utility of 0.80 is acceptable.

3.38 The problem faced by Silverman is

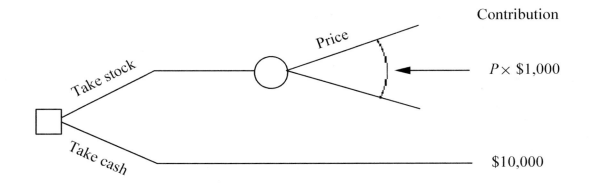

The cumulative stock price probability distribution is given below. A five point discrete approximation is

Price	Probability
8.00	0.2
11.40	0.2
14.00	0.2
15.50	0.2
19.50	0.2

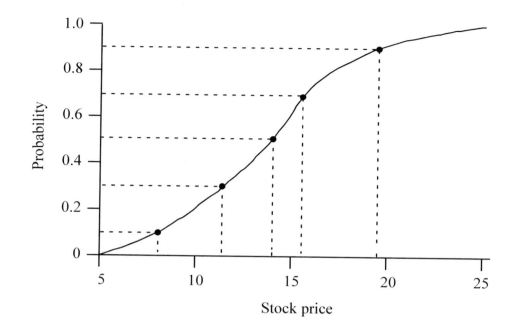

Silverman's preference curve consists of the following points:

$U(25K) = 1.0, \quad U(9K) = 0.5, \quad U(3K) = 0.2, \quad U(0) = 0$

$U(12K) = 0.5U(25K) + 0.5U(3K) = 0.5 \times 1 + 0.5 \times 0.2 = 0.6$

$U(17K) = 0.5U(25K) + 0.5U(12K) = 0.5 \times 1 + 0.5 \times 0.6 = 0.8$

which can be graphed as

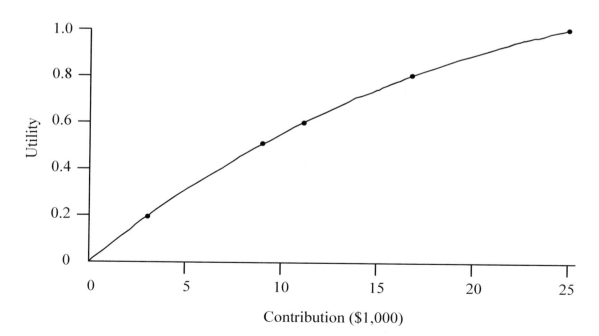

The certainty equivalent is

Price	Contribution	Utility	Probability
8.0	$8,000	0.46	0.2
11.4	11,400	0.59	0.2
14.0	14,000	0.69	0.2
15.5	15,500	0.78	0.2
19.5	19,500	0.88	0.2
	Expected utility:	0.68	
	Certainty equivalent:	$13,600	

Decision: Take the stock

3.39 The manager has the choice of the sure thing (call this scenario A) versus the gamble (call this scenario B).

Alternative A: a sure amount of $5,000
Alternative B: a gamble that offers a 70-30 chance of winning $10,000 or nothing.

$$U(B) = 0.7U(\$10,000) + 0.3U(\$0) = 0.7(100) + 0.3(1) = 0.3$$

In order to be indifferent between A and B,

$$U(A) = U(\$5,000) = U(B) = 70.3 \rightarrow \text{utility index for } \$5,000 \text{ is } 70.3.$$

3.40 Let C be the alternative of getting $5,000 for sure.

D be the gamble with a 60-40 chance of winning either $10,000 or $1,000.

Because the manager is indifferent between C and D,

$$U(\$5,000) = 70.3 = 0.6U(\$10,000) + 0.4U(\$1,000) \rightarrow$$

$$U(\$1,000) = 25.75$$

That is, the utility index for $1,000 is 25.75.

3.41 From point (1) in the problem statement, we have

$$U(\$10,000) = 0.5U(\$30,000) + 0.5U(-\$1,000)$$

$$= 0.5(30) + 0.5(-2) = 14$$

Let p be the probability that the payoff for the new risky venture is $0. Since the executive is indifferent between the certain $10,000 and the gamble with outcome $0 or $20,000 with probabilities p and $(1-p)$, respectively,

$$U(\$10,000) = 14 = pU(\$0) + (1-p)U(\$20,000) = p(0) + (1-p)(20) \rightarrow$$

$$p = 0.3$$

Therefore, the probability combination between $0 and $20,000 should be 30-70.

3.42 Investing $3,000 can result in the following:

- making $0, $U(\$0) = 0$ with probability 0.2

- making $2,000, $U(\$2,000) = 25$ with probability 0.3

- making $4,000, $U(\$4,000) = 35$ with probability 0.2

- making $6,000, $U(\$6,000) = 40$ with probability 0.3

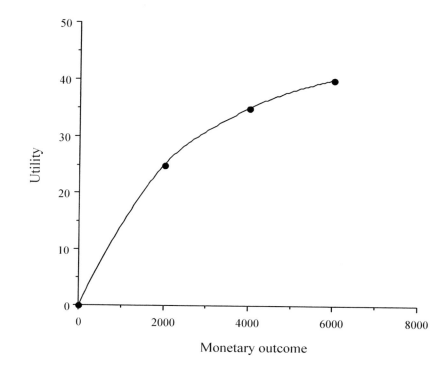

Ms Gumm has 2 alternatives: A, don't invest; B, invest the $3,000

EMV(A) = $3,000; EU(A) = $U(\$3,000)$ = 30
EMV(B) = 0.2(0) + 0.3($2,000) + 0.2($4,000) + 0.3($6,000) = $3,200
EU(B) = 0.2(0) + 0.3(25) + 0.2(35) + 0.3(40) = 26.5

Now, EMV(A) < EMV(B) but EU(A) > EU(B). Therefore, Frances will be happier if she does not make the investment.

3.43 (a) The manager's utility curve is presented below. From the statement of the problem, he is indifferent between receiving $11,000 for certain and the gamble with a 60-40 chance of winning $5,000 or $20,000, respectively. Therefore,

$U(\$11,000) = 6 = 0.6U(\$5,000) + 0.4U(\$20,000) = 0.6U(\$5,000) + 0.4(10) \rightarrow$
$U(\$5,000) = 3.33$

(b)   Let X be the amount of cash that will make the manager indifferent to the gamble.

$$U(\$X) = 0.2U(-\$2{,}000) + 0.3U(\$0) + 0.4U(\$3{,}000) + 0.1U(\$10{,}000)$$

$$U(\$X) = 0.2(-3) + 0.3(0) + 0.4(2) + 0.1(5) = 0.7$$

From the utility curve, we get $X \cong \$1{,}000$.

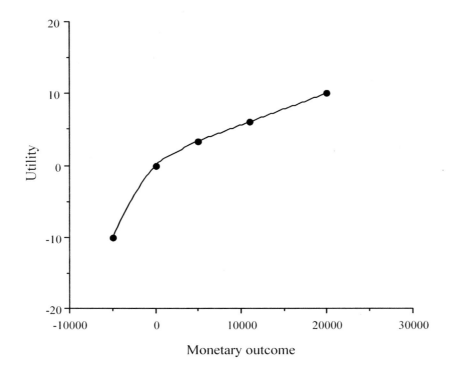

(c)   Let p be the probability of receiving $0 and $1 - p$ be the probability of receiving $20,000. To find p we must solve

$$U(\$11{,}000) = 6 = pU(\$0) + (1-p)U(\$20{,}000) = p(0) + (1-p)10 \;\rightarrow$$

$$p = 0.4$$

implying that a 40-60 gamble with either $0 or $20,000 as the payoff would make the manager indifferent between the certain $11,000.

(d) Assumptions: (1) all axioms associated with Bernoulli's principle apply, (2) a decision is only going to be made once so expected utility rather than expected value should be the decision criterion, (3) the approximate utility curve is an accurate representation of the decision maker's true utility curve.

U(buying a new machine) $= 0.8U(\$15,000) + 0.2U(-\$1,000) = 0.8(8) + 0.2(-1) = 6.2$

U(using the old machine) $= U(\$10,000) = 5$

Because the utility index for buying a new machine is higher, the manager should select that alternative.

CHAPTER

4. LIFE-CYCLE COSTING

4.1 The cost of a used car is highly correlated with the following variables:

t = age of the car $\qquad$ $1 \leq t \leq 5$ (years)

V = volume of engine $\qquad$ $1000 \leq V \leq 2500$ (cubic centimeters)

D = number of doors $\qquad$ $D = 2, 3, 4, 5$

A = accessories and style $\quad$ $A = 1, 2, 3, 4, 5, 6$ (qualitative)

Using regression analysis, the following relationship between the cost of a car and the four independent variables was found:

$$\text{purchase cost} = \left(1 + \frac{1}{t}\right) \times V \times \left(\frac{D}{2} + A\right)$$

(a) Cost as a function of the four variables. In each case, it is assumed that all other variables are held constant.

1. Cost as a function of age

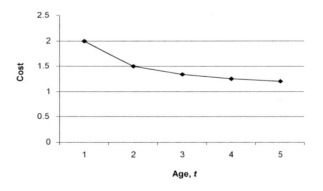

2. Cost as a function of number of doors

No. of doors	Cost
1	$A + 0.5$
2	$A + 1$
3	$A + 1.5$
4	$A + 2$
5	$A + 2.5$

3. Cost as a function of volume

Volume	Cost
1000	*C*
1500	1.5*C*
2000	2*C*
2500	2.5*C*
5000	5*C*

where *C* is the cost when *V* = 1000 and all other variables are held constant.

4. Cost as a function of style

Style	Cost
1	*D*/2 + 1
2	*D*/2 + 2
3	*D*/2 + 3
4	*D*/2 + 4
5	*D*/2 + 5
6	*D*/2 + 6

(b) All the variables but time are linearly related to cost. If either *V*, *D* or *A* is doubled for example, so is the cost. For age, we note that the derivative of the purchasing cost with respect to t is $-1/t^2$, so as t increases the cost decreases by a factor of t^2. For example, doubling t decreases the cost by 4. Thus we conclude that t has the greatest impact on cost.

(c)   The following combinations are feasible for $5000 or less.

t	*V*	*D*	*A*
5	1000 to 2083	2	1
5	1000 to 1666	3	1
5	1000 to 1388	4	1
5	1000 to 1190	5	1
5	1000 to 1388	2	2
5	1000 to 1190	3	2
5	1000 to 1041	4	2
5	1000 to 1041	2	3
4	1000 to 1999	2	1
4	1000 to 1599	3	1
4	1000 to 1332	4	1
4	1000 to 1142	5	1
3	1000 to 1879	2	1
3	1000 to 1503	3	1

3	1000 to 1252	4	1
3	1000 to 1073	5	1
2	1000 to 1666	2	1
2	1000 to 1332	3	1
2	1000 to 1070	4	1
1	1000 to 1249	2	1
4	1000 to 1332	2	2
3	1000 to 1073	3	2

(d) Assuming that the car is for your family four doors is a must and the largest engine possible is desired. The best configuration that satisfies these criteria is a 5-year old car with a style rating of 1, an engine volume of 1388, and 4 doors.

(e) Assuming that for each option listed in (c) the largest engine is selected (thus, the purchasing cost is $5000 for all cases considered here), the maintenance and operating costs for the different models is listed below. If we also assume that minimizing annual cost is the objective, the best choice is a 2-year old car with 4 doors, $A = 1$, and an engine volume of 1070 cc. The corresponding model is marked by an asterisk in the table.

t	V	D	A	Maintenance cost	Operating cost	Total annual cost
5	2083	2	1	31245	576	31821
5	1666	3	1	24990	799	23789
5	1388	4	1	20820	1022	21842
5	1190	5	1	17850	1252	19102
5	1388	2	2	20820	546	21366
5	1190	3	2	17850	777	18627
5	1041	4	2	15615	1008	16623
5	1041	2	3	15615	528	16143
4	1999	2	1	23988	480	24468
4	1599	3	1	19188	653	19841
4	1332	4	1	15984	830	16814
4	1142	5	1	13704	1008	14712
4	1332	2	2	15984	446	16430
3	1879	2	1	16911	374	17285
3	1503	3	1	13527	504	14031
3	1252	4	1	11277	633	11910
3	1073	5	1	9657	768	10425
3	1252	2	2	11268	346	11614
3	1073	3	2	9657	480	10137
2	1666	2	1	9996	269	10265
2	1332	3	1	7992	350	8342
2	1070	4	1	6420	432	6852*
1	1249	2	1	7494	153	7647

4.2 A construction project consists of 10 identical units. The cost of the first unit is $25,000 and a learning curve of 90% applies to the cost and the duration of consecutive units. Assume that the first unit takes 6 months to finish and that the project is financed by a loan taken at the beginning of the project at an annual interest rate of 10%.

(a) To determine whether the units should be constructed in or in parallel, we will consider both cases.

   1. A sequential schedule:

      The first step is to look up the cumulative learning curve value in Table 9B-2 for 10 repetitions and a 90% learning curve. The corresponding value is 7.994.

      Total cost = $25,000 × 7.994 = $199,850

      Total duration = 6 × 7.994 = 47.964 months = 4 years

To determine the net present value building the 10 units in sequence, let us assume that the total cost is incurred in equal amounts over the four years. Then

$$\text{NPV} = \frac{\$199,850}{4}(P/A, 10\%, 4) = \$49,962.5 \times 3.1699 = \$158,376$$

2. All units constructed in parallel:

Total cost = $\$25,000 \times 10 = \$250,000$
Total duration = 0.5 years.
NPV of project ($250,000 for 0.5 years at 10%)

$$= \$250,000(P/F, 10\%, 0.5)$$

$$= \$250,000 \times \frac{1}{(1+0.1)^{0.5}} = \frac{\$250,000}{1.0488} = \$238,366$$

(b) The total cost is minimized by the sequential schedule.

4.3   Three different approaches are offered.

I. The traditional classification

    1. Total cost
        1.1 Direct cost
            1.1.1 Direct labor cost
            1.1.2 Direct material cost
            1.1.3 Other direct cost
        1.2 Indirect costs
            1.2.1 Indirect labor cost
            1.2.2 Indirect material cost
            1.2.3 Other indirect costs
        1.3 Other costs

II. A cost structure based on the project life cycle

    1. Total cost
        1.1 Cost of design
            1.1.1 Conceptual design
            1.1.2 Detailed design
            1.1.3 Cost of a model
        1.2 Cost of construction
            1.2.1 Foundation
            1.2.2 Structure
            1.2.3 Finish
        1.3 Cost of landscaping
        1.4 Cost of operation
        1.5 Cost of maintenance

1.6 Cost of renovations
1.7 Cost of phase out

III. A cost classification based on the project CBS

1. Total cost
    1.1 Cost of internal resources
        1.1.1 Design and engineering
        1.1.2 Project management
        1.1.3 Operations and maintenance
    1.2 Cost of consultants and subcontractors
        1.2.1 Cost of architects and engineers
        1.2.2 Cost of construction contractors
        1.2.3 Cost of consulting
        1.2.4 Cost of maintenance contractors
        1.2.5 Cost of security and operation contractors

4.4 No solution.

4.5 The cost breakdown structure and the cash flow for an office building is given in the following table.

Description	Code	Start date	Finish date	Cost ($10K)
Total Cost	999	11-01-03	04-18-04	4970.00
1. Design	100	11-01-03	03-04-04	62.00
Conceptual	110	11-01-03	12-03-03	14.00
Direct labor	111	11-01-03	12-03-03	9.00
Direct material	112	11-01-03	12-03-03	1.00
Indirect labor	112	11-01-03	12-03-03	3.00
Indirect material	114	11-01-03	12-03-03	1.00
Detailed	120	12-06-03	02-11-04	32.00
Direct labor	121	12-06-03	02-11-04	23.00
Direct material	122	12-06-03	02-11-04	2.00
Indirect labor	123	12-06-03	02-11-04	6.00
Indirect material	124	12-06-03	02-11-04	1.00
Model	130	02-14-04	03-04-04	16.00
Direct labor	131	02-14-04	03-04-04	5.00
Direct material	132	02-14-04	03-04-04	8.00
Indirect labor	133	02-14-04	03-04-04	2.00
Indirect material	134	02-14-04	03-04-04	1.00
2. Construction	200	03-07-04	11-11-04	2573.00
Foundation	210	03-07-04	05-27-04	435.00
Direct labor	211	03-07-04	05-27-04	124.00
Direct material	212	03-07-04	05-27-04	235.00
Indirect labor	213	03-07-04	05-27-04	21.00
Indirect material	214	03-07-04	05-27-04	55.00

Strucuture	220	03-07-04	08-12-04	878.00
Direct labor	221	03-07-04	08-12-04	354.00
Direct material	222	03-07-04	08-12-04	467.00
Indirect labor	223	03-07-04	08-12-04	45.00
Indirect material	224	03-07-04	08-12-04	12.00
Finish	230	08-15-04	11-11-04	1260.00
Direct labor	231	08-15-04	11-11-04	235.00
Direct material	232	08-15-04	11-11-04	987.00
Indirect labor	233	08-15-04	11-11-04	24.00
Indirect material	234	08-15-04	11-11-04	14.00
3. Landscaping	300	11-14-04	12-23-04	188.00
Direct labor	311	11-14-04	12-23-04	34.00
Direct material	312	11-14-04	12-23-04	125.00
Indirect labor	313	11-14-04	12-23-04	22.00
Indirect material	314	11-14-04	12-23-04	7.00
4. Operations	400	12-26-04	02-21-04	658.00
Direct labor	411	12-26-04	02-21-04	350.00
Direct material	412	12-26-04	02-21-04	270.00
Indirect labor	413	12-26-04	02-21-04	12.00
Indirect material	414	12-26-04	02-21-04	26.00
5. Maintenance	500	12-26-04	02-21-04	486.00
Direct labor	511	12-26-04	02-21-04	240.00
Direct material	512	12-26-04	02-21-04	200.00
Indirect labor	513	12-26-04	02-21-04	12.00
Indirect material	514	12-26-04	02-21-04	34.00
6. Renovations	600	11-01-03	12-28-04	931.00
Direct labor	611	11-01-03	12-28-04	380.00
Direct material	612	11-01-03	12-28-04	450.00
Indirect labor	613	11-01-03	12-28-04	34.00
Indirect material	614	11-01-03	12-28-04	67.00
7. Phase Out	700	02-24-04	04-18-04	72.00
Direct labor	711	02-24-04	04-18-04	35.00
Direct material	712	02-24-04	04-18-04	13.00
Indirect labor	713	02-24-04	04-18-04	15.00
Indirect material	714	02-24-04	04-18-04	9.00

4.6 Pareto analysis

Description	Cost ($10K)	Cumulative cost	% of total cost	Cumulative %
Construction	2573	2573	51.7	51.7
Renovation	931	3504	18.7	70.4
Operation	658	4162	13.2	83.6
Maintenance	486	4648	9.8	93.4
Landscaping	188	4836	3.7	97.1
Phase out	72	4908	1.5	98.6
Design	62	4970	1.4	100

Group A: Constructing and renovation
Group B: Operation
Group C: Maintenance, landscaping, phase out and design

4.7 A cost estimate for three weeks vacation in Europe:

1. Transportation
    1.1 Flight-round trip to Europe $1500
    1.2 Car rental (3 weeks) $1200
    1.3 Fuel etc. $300
    1.4 Taxis $100
    1.5 Parking $100
        Subtotal $3200

2. Food and lodging
    2.1 Hotels (20 nights) × $100 $2000
    2.2 Meals ($50/day) × 20 days $1000
        Subtotal $3000

3. Admission fees $500

4. Miscellaneous
    4.1 Insurance $500
    4.2 Tips $300
    4.3 reserve $500
        Subtotal $1300

        Grand total $8000

4.8 In the following model no cost estimates are presented because the major factor is the length of time the car is either owned or rented. Major components of the cost breakdown structure are listed below.

Cost component	Buy	Rent
Purchase cost	$B	–
Rent	–	$R
Operations:		
maintenance	$M_1	$M_2
insurance	$I_1	$I_2
Salvage-cost	$S	–
Tax benefits	$T_1	$T_2

When the planning horizon is short, it is usually better to rent. In the long run, thoug, it is better to purchase the car and incur the escalating O&M costs.

4.9 Natasha Gurdin is debating which of two possible models of a car to buy (A or B), being indifferent with regard to their technical performance. She has been told that the average monthly cost of owning model A, based on an LCC analysis, is $500.

(a) Assuming all costs are stated in terms of present values, the total present value of expenses for model B is as follows.

Purchase price			$23,000
Maintenance	$1,100 × 4	=	4,400
Operational cost	$90 × 48	=	4,320
Car insurance	$1,400 × 4	=	5,600
Repair costs due to failures	$650 × 48/14	=	2,229
Total expenses			$39,549
Resale value			$13,000
Net expenses			$26,549

The monthly cost of owing model B for a four-year period is:

$$\frac{\$26,549}{48} = \$533$$

Therefore, from an LCC point of view, model A is less expensive by $553 – $500 = $53/mo.

(b) A possible LCC model in present value terms might be:

$$\text{LCC} = \text{Purchase price} + (\text{Annual maintenance}) \times (P/A,\ i\%,\ n) + (\text{Operational costs per}$$
$$\text{month}) \times (P/A,\ i\%/12,\ n/12) + \text{Insurance} \times (P/A,\ i\%/2,\ n/2) + (\text{Damage due to}$$
$$\text{failures}) \times (P/A,\ i\%/N,\ N) - \text{Resale value} \times (P/F,\ i\%,\ n)$$

where $i\%$ = nominal interest rate

n = number of years car is owned

$N = 12n/\text{MTBF}$ (mean time between failures)

In the model, it assumed that insurance premiums are paid twice a year and all costs are constant from period to period; i.e., there are no cost increases over the life cycle of the car. In the case of O&M costs, at least, it might be better to assume a gradient increase.

4.10 – 4.15 No solutions.

CHAPTER

5. PROJECT SCREENING AND SELECTION

5.1 Let us consider the situation in which a graduating senior has to decide if he wants to go to graduate school or take a job. The four major factors affecting the decision are employment opportunities, intellectual satisfaction, earning potential and growth potential. Given below is a tabulation of the criteria, their weights and scores for each alternative. The scores for each criterion range from 1 to 3.

	Grad School	Job	Weight
Intellectual satisfaction	3	1	0.4
Employment opportunities	3	2	0.1
Earning potential	2	3	0.3
Growth potential	3	2	0.2
Score	2.7	1.9	1.0

Among the four criteria considered, the earning potential and growth potential have uncertainty associated with them due to the long-term implications. Choosing a profession, such as teaching or government service, where salaries are determined by a schedule or index might reduce the uncertainty.

5.2 The three cars under consideration are: 2004 Toyota Corolla (A), 2004 Ford Escort (B), and 2006 Hyundai Excel (C). Using a scoring scale of 1-3 might produce the following results.

	A	B	C
Initial cost	2	3	3
Reliability	3	2	1
Maintenance cost	3	2	3
Resale value	3	2	1
Score	11	9	8

5.3 (a) If only benefit-cost ratio is used, we would choose an area which has the highest annual earning potential to annual cost ratio.

(b) If cost-effectiveness analysis is used, we would have to take into account the affordability of the option too. For instance, even though an MBA degree may be the most attractive in terms of its earning potential, it may be too expensive to get for many people.

5.4 The three options we consider are:

Option A: Rent a U-haul truck and move the stuff yourself
Option B: Hire a moving company to do the job

Option C: Have the items packed and unpacked by professionals and move them yourself

Using a scoring and weighted scoring model with a 1-3 scale gives:

	A	B	C	Weight
Cost	1	3	2	0.4
Effort required	3	1	2	0.2
Time taken	3	1	2	0.1
Damage to items	3	1	2	0.3
Score	10	6	8	1.0
Weighted score	1.9	1.8	2.0	

5.5 (a)

	Product			
	A	B	C	Weight
Development Cost	1	2	4	0.1
Sales	4	5	3	0.15
Producibility	1	2	3	0.1
Competition	5	4	2	0.15
Technical Risk	1	2	4	0.2
Patent Protection	2	2	4	0.1
Compatibility	4	2	2	0.2
Score	2.75	2.75	3.05	1.0

Score(A) = (.1)(1) + (.15)(4) + (.1)(1) + (.15)(5) + (.2)(1) + (.1)(2) + (.2)(4) = 2.75

Score(B) = (.1)(2) + (.15)(5) + (.1)(2) + (.15)(4) + (.2)(2) + (.1)(2) + (.2)(2) = 2.75

Score(C) = (.1)(4) + (.15)(3) + (.1)(3) + (.15)(2) + (.2)(4) + (.1)(4) + (.2)(2) = 3.05

(b) Let RSW = rank sum weights and RRW = rank reciprocal weights.

	A	B	C	Rank	RSW	RRW
Development Cost	1	2	4	5	0.11	0.08
Sales	4	5	3	3	0.18	0.13
Producibility	1	2	3	6	0.07	0.06
Competition	5	4	2	4	0.14	0.10
Technical Risk	1	2	4	1	0.25	0.39
Patent Protection	2	2	4	7	0.04	0.05
Compatibility	4	2	2	2	0.25	0.19
RSW Score	2.77	2.82	3.05			
RRW Score	2.41	2.59	3.43			

(c)   *Advantages:* This method allows for an objective measure of the various factors. By specifying weights and scores, the method forces the evaluator to look at all factors. It gives a weighted score for the projects, based on the factors.

Disadvantages: Scores and weights are subjective estimates. Factors are, by their nature, extremely hard to quantify, even in a subjective manner. The method assumes the scores are linearly related (i.e., that "good" lies exactly between "excellent" and "poor").

5.6   (a) Let p_T be the probability of technical success and p_C be the probability of commercial success. Then the expected ROI(X) for product X can be found by finding i that makes NPV(X) = 0.

$$NPV(X) = TDC - (p_T \times p_C \times \text{annual volume} \times \text{profit})(P/A, i, n) = 0$$

$$NPV(A) = \$50,000 - (0.9 \times 0.6 \times 10,000 \times \$2.64)(P/A, i, 10) = 0$$
For $i = 25\%$, we have
$$\$50,000 - (\$14,256)(3.505) = \$50,000 - \$49,967 \cong 0$$

$$NPV(B) = \$70,000 - (0.8 \times 0.8 \times 8,000 \times \$3.91)(P/A, i, 6) = 0$$
For $i = 18\%$, we have
$$\$70,000 - (20,019)(3.498) = \$70,000 - \$70,026 \cong 0$$

$$NPV(C) = \$100,000 - (0.7 \times 0.9 \times 6,000 \times \$5.96)(P/A, i, 12) = 0$$
For $i = 20\%$, we have
$$\$100,000 - (\$22,529)(3.498) = \$100,000 - \$100,010 \cong 0$$

(b)

Rank	From Exercise 5.5 Product	From Exercise 5.6 Product
1	C	A
2	A	C
3	B	B

5.7   (a)   PW of Benefits $= 60,000(P/A, 5\%, 10) + 64,000(P/A, 5\%, 10)(P/F, 5\%, 10) + 66,000(P/A, 5\%, 20)(P/F, 5\%, 20) + 70,000(P/A, 5\%, 10)(P/F, 5\%, 40)$

$= 60,000(7.722) + 64,000(7.722)(0.6139) + 66,000(12.462)(0.3769) + 70,000(7.722)(0.1420)$

$= \underline{\$1,153,468}$

For B/C ratio = 1, PW of Cost = PW of Benefits

Justified capital expenditure $= 1,153,468 - 15,000(P/A, 5\%, 50)$

$= 1,153,468 - 15,000(18.256) = \underline{\$879,628}$

(b) Same equation as in part (a), except use 8% interest.

PW of Benefits $= 60,000(6.710) + 64,000(6.710)(0.4632) + 66,000(9.818)(0.2145) +$
$70,000(6.710)(0.0460) = \underline{\$762,116}$

Justified capital expenditure $= 762,116 - 15,000(12.233) = \underline{\$578,621}$

5.8 Overpass cost = $1,800,000; salvage value = $100,000; $n = 30$; $i = 6\%$. If built,

Benefits to the public

time savings	400 trucks $\times \dfrac{2}{60} \times \$18/hr$ =	$240 per day
1000 vehicles/day	600 others $\times \dfrac{2}{60} \times \$5/hr$ =	$100 per day
		$340 per day

Benefits to the state

saving in accident investigation costs, etc. $\quad = \quad$ \$6,000 per year

Combined benefits

benefits to public + state: $340(365 days) + $6,000 $\quad = \quad$ \$130,100 per year

Benefits to the railroad

saving in crossing guard expense $\qquad$ $48,000 per year
saving in accident case expense $\qquad$ $60,000 per year
$\qquad$ $108,000 per year

Should the overpass be built?

Benefit-cost ratio analysis

Annual cost (EUAC) $= \$1,700,000(A/P, 6\%, 30) + \$100,000(0.06)$
$= \$1,700,000(0.0726) + \$6,000$
$= \$129,420$

Annual benefits (EUAB) $= \$130,100 + \$108,000$
$= \$238,100$

$$B/C = \frac{EUAB}{EUAC} = \frac{\$238,100}{\$129,420} = 1.84$$

With a B/C ratio > 1, the project is economically justified.

Allocation of the $1,800,000 cost

The railroad should contribute to the project in proportion to the benefits received.

$$\text{PW of cost} = \$1,800,000 - 100,000(P/F, 6\%, 30)$$

$$= \$1,800,000 - 100,000(0.1741) = \$1,782,590$$

The railroad portion would be: $\dfrac{108,000}{238,100}$ ($\$1,782,590$) $=$ $\$808,570$

The state portion would be:

$$\dfrac{130,100}{238,100} (\$1,782,590) + \$100,000(P/F, 6\%, 30) = \underline{\$991,430}$$

$$\$1,800,000$$

While this problem is a simplified representation of the situation, it illustrates a realistic statement of benefits and an economic analysis solution to the allocation of costs.

5.9

	Existing	Plan A	Plan B	Plan C
Length (miles)	10	10	10	10.3
Number of lanes	2	4	4	4
Average ADT	20,000	20,000	20,000	20,000
autos	19,000	19,000	19,000	19,000
trucks	1,000	1,000	1,000	1,000
Time savings (minutes)				
autos		2	3	5
trucks		1	3	4
Accident rate/MVM	4.58	2.50	2.40	2.30
Initial cost per mile (P)	\$0	\$450,000	\$650,000	\$800,000
Annual maintenance				
per lane per mile	\$1,500	\$1,250	\$1,000	\$1,000
Total annual maintenance	\$30,000	\$50,000	\$40,000	\$41,200
EUAC of initial cost				
= (P × miles)(A/P, 5%, 20)				
= (P × miles)(0.0802)	\$0	\$360,900	\$521,300	\$660,850
Total annual cost of EUAC				
and maintenance	\$30,000	\$410,900	\$561,300	\$702,050

Annual Incremental Operating Costs Due to Distance

None for Plans A and B; same length as existing road

Plan C:	Autos	$19,000 \times 365 \times 0.3$ mi $\times \$0.06$	$= \$124,830$
	Trucks	$1,000 \times 365 \times 0.3$ mi $\times \$0.18$	$= \underline{\$19,710}$
			$\$144,540$/year

Annual Accident Savings Compared to Existing Highway

Plan A: $(4.58 - 2.50)(10^{-6})(10$ mi$)(365$ days$)(20,000$ ADT$)(\$1,200) = \$182,200$

Plan B: $(4.58 - 2.40)(10^{-6})(10$ mi$)(365$ days$)(20,000$ ADT$)(\$1,200) = \$190,970$

Plan C: $(4.58 - 2.30)(10^{-6})(10.3$ mi$)(365$ days$)(20,000$ ADT$)(\$1,200) = \$205,720$

Time Savings Benefits to Road Users Compared to Existing Highway

Plan A:

Autos	$19,000 \times 365$ days $\times 2$ min $\times \$0.03$	=	$416,100
Trucks	$1,000 \times 365$ days $\times 1$ min $\times \$0.15$	=	54,750
			$470,850

Plan B:

Autos	$19,000 \times 365$ days $\times 3$ min $\times \$0.03$	=	$624,150
Trucks	$1,000 \times 365$ days $\times 3$ min $\times \$0.15$	=	164,250
			$788,400

Plan C:

Autos	$19,000 \times 365$ days $\times 5$ min $\times \$0.03$	=	$1,040,250
Trucks	$1,000 \times 365$ days $\times 4$ min $\times \$0.15$	=	219,000
			$1,259,250

Summary of Annual Costs and Benefits

	Existing	Plan A	Plan B	Plan C
Annual highway costs	$30,000	$410,900	$561,300	$702,050
Annual benefits				
Accident savings		182,200	190,970	205,720
Time savings		470,850	788,400	1,259,250
Additional operating cost*				−144,540
Total annual benefits:		653,050	979,370	1,320,430

*User costs considered as a disbenefit

Benefit-Cost Ratios

Plan A rather than Existing: $B/C = \dfrac{653,050}{410,900 - 30,000} = 1.71$

Plan B rather than Plan A: $B/C = \dfrac{979,370 - 653,050}{561,300 - 410,900} = 2.17$

Plan C rather than Plan B: $B/C = \dfrac{1,320,430 - 979,370}{702,050 - 561,300} = 2.42 \Rightarrow$ Plan C preferred

5.10 This problem will require some thought on how to structure the analysis. This is a situation of providing the necessary capacity when it is needed — in other words, *fixed output*. Computing the cost is easy, but what is the benefit?

One cannot compute the B/C ratio for either alternative, but the incremental B/C ratio may be computed on the difference between the alternatives.

Year	A Half capacity tunnel now plus second half capacity tunnel in 20 years	B Full capacity tunnel	B – A Difference between alternatives
0	– $300,000	– $500,000	– $200,000
10	–16,000	–20,000	– 4,000
20	–16,000	– 20,000	+396,000
	– 400,000		
30	– 32,000	– 20,000	+12,000
40	– 32,000	– 20,000	+12,000
50	0	0	0

$$\frac{\Delta B}{\Delta C} = \frac{396,000(P\,/\,F,\,5\%,\,20)+12,000(P\,/\,F,5\%,\,30)+12,000(P\,/\,F,\,5\%,\,40)}{200,000+4,000(P\,/\,F,\,5\%,\,10)}$$

$$= \frac{153,733}{202,456} = 0.76$$

This is an undesirable increment of investment. Build the half-capacity tunnel now.

5.11 (a) There are several factors to be considered when deciding on an acceptable noise level since prolonged exposure to intense noise can cause serious health problems. The risks associated with accepting higher decibel levels would be possible damage to employees' hearing leading perhaps to expensive law suits against the company, and agitated and unnerved workers leading to poor job performance and reduced output. Noise levels can be kept low by installing special noise reduction equipment, using quieter machinery, insulating rooms, and so forth. These measures may be expensive, however, so a trade-off analysis should be undertaken to determine the best course of action.

(b) Unlike a shop floor, commercial aircraft do not operate in a controlled environment. The people living near airports, as well as the passengers and crew, are constantly exposed to aircraft noise. Typically, every city or county imposes acceptable noise levels for aircraft so designers and flight control personnel must work within these limits.

5.12 Nationwide testing of health care workers for AIDS would incur costs for periodic notification, collecting and disposing of specimens, performing the tests, maintaining records, and administering the program. Each facility would have to set up their own data base and establish procedures for scheduling workers, reporting results, and taking action when called for. It might also be desirable to develop a national data base. Expected benefits would be a greater awareness of the risks of contacting AIDS from health care workers and perhaps a decrease in the number of persons who contract the disease in this manner. This might translate directly into a reduction in expenditures associated with taking care of AIDS patients.

One approach to implementing a national plan would begin by selecting one or two major facilities as test beds and establishing the necessary infrastructure; that is, policies, procedures, data bases, and reporting schemes. The next step would be to formalize what was learned and develop a schedule for phasing in all facilities and workers. The schedule might be hierarchical starting with major health care facilities, such as hospitals and health maintenance organizations, and progressing downward in size to the smaller facilities, such as diagnostic clinics and individual offices, and finishing with itinerant personnel, such as school nurses. The costs of the plan would depend in part on the mechanisms set up to do conduct the tests, the frequency of testing, system development time, the number of laboratories required to perform the tests, and the resistance encountered at state and local levels.

The risk of not testing would be a greater number of persons contracting AIDS from their health care workers. Collectively, the country would pay more for taking care of these patients. In addition, there is a social cost associated with the anxiety surrounding the fear of getting the disease during a hospital stay or while in a dentist's office, for instance. On the other hand, early diagnosis might prematurely lead to firing of health care workers who pose no danger to the public. Such action would reduce incomes and perhaps increase the burden on the welfare system.

5.13 This problem is intended to be open ended. Let us begin by considering the two possibilities: option A involves complete replacement of the existing system with a new one; option B involves a two-phase plan. In the first phase of option B, the new system would be partially installed and after one year of operations the second phase would be implemented if conditions were favorable.

Associated costs include acquisition, personnel retraining, and loss of production time during startup. Benefits accrue in the form of saving in inventory costs and payroll due to a potential reduction in labor force. External risks might depend on the state of the economy which would affect company's sales. Internal risks might include worker and management acceptance, problems with implementation, and data base maintenance. The costs, benefits, and external risks for the various options are tabulated below. Assume that the probability that the economy will be good is 0.7.

Option	Cost	Benefits if good economy	Benefits if bad economy
A: replace	$100,000	$200,000	$50,000
B: phase 1	$50,000	$80,000	$30,000
B: phase 2	$75,000	$125,000	$65,000
B: no phase 2		$25,000	$10,000

The corresponding decision tree is

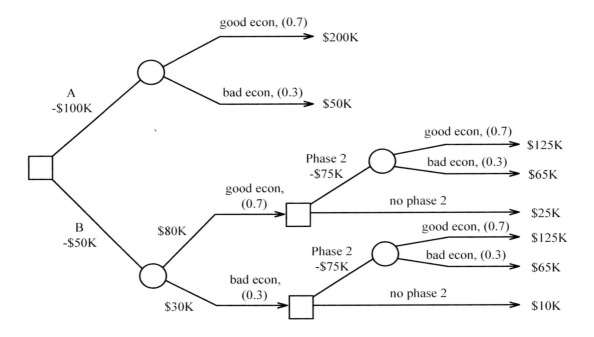

5.14 Let D1 = stock 100 boards, D2 = stock 120 boards, D3 = stock 130 boards. Let d represent the demand for boards. From the data we know that each board sold returns $0.45 in profit; that is, profit = revenue – preparation cost = $1.05 – $0.60 = $0.45. Now, assume that the reprocessing cost of an unused board is incurred on day 2. In other words, if a board is prepared today but is not used until tomorrow, its cost ($0.60) will be incurred today while its reprocessing cost ($0.55) will be incurred tomorrow.

Given below is a decision tree for the problem. The optimal decision is D2 to stock 120 boards.

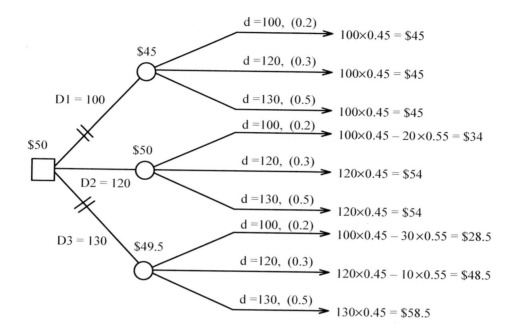

An additional consideration might be lost sales. If you stock 120 boards and the demand is 130, you forgo $(130 - 120) \times \$0.45 = \$4.5$. This value would then be subtracted from the revenue of $54 giving a net of $49.5 for the corresponding branch in the tree.

5.15 Using the costs computed in the previous problem, we get the following decision tree.

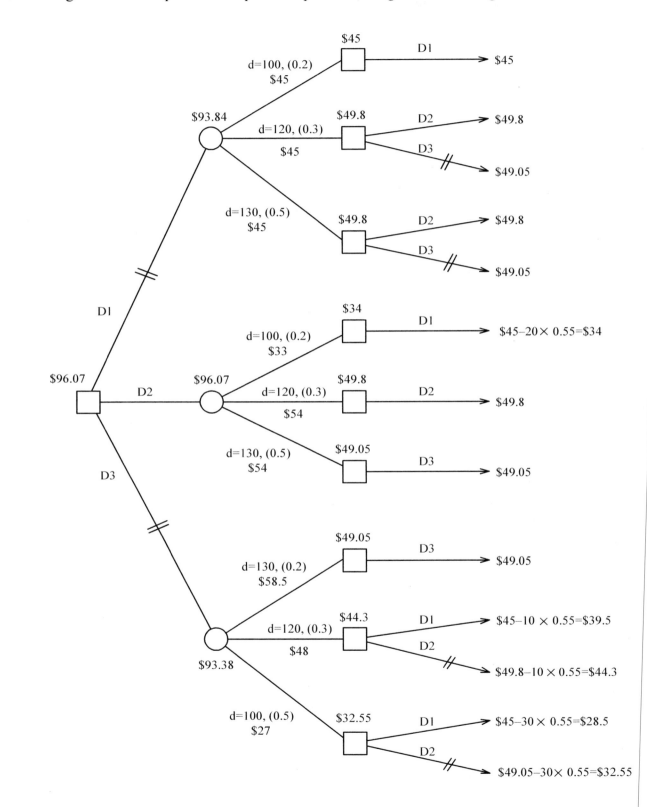

5.16 Let a_1 = produce internally, a_2 = subcontract, and $a*$ = optimal strategy.

(a)

(b)

Action	Future demand			EV(a_i)
	Low	Average	High	
Produce	140	120	90	113
Subcontract	100	110	160	124
Probability	0.10	0.60	0.30	

(c) If future demand is known exactly, then the expected value of perfect information can be computed as follows:

$$EVPI = (0.10)(100) + (0.60)(110) + (0.30)(90) = 103$$

That is, we take the expected value of costs using the lowest values for each possible outcome.

5.17 (a) To determine the optimal action given a pessimistic forecast, f_3, we must first compute the conditional probabilities of the three states of nature associated with future demand.

$$p(s_1 \mid f_3) = \frac{p(f_3 \mid s_1)\, p(s_1)}{p(f_3 \mid s_1)p(s_1) + p(f_3 \mid s_2)p(s_2) + p(f_3 \mid s_3)p(s_3)}$$

$$= \frac{(0.6)(0.10)}{(0.6)(0.10) + (0.2)(0.60) + (0.1)(0.30)} = \frac{0.06}{0.21} = 0.286$$

$$p(s_2 \mid f_3) = \frac{p(f_3 \mid s_2)\, p(s_2)}{p(f_3)} = \frac{(0.2)(0.60)}{0.21} = 0.571$$

$$p(s_3 \mid f_3) = 1 - p(s_1 \mid f_3) - p(s_2 \mid f_3) = 1 - 0.286 - 0.571 = 0.143$$

Let a_1 = produce and a_2 = subcontract, we have

$$EV[a_1 \mid f_3] = (0.286)(140) + (0.571)(120) + (0.143)(90) = 121.43$$

$$EV[a_2 \mid f_3] = (0.286)(100) + (0.571)(110) + (0.143)(160) = 114.25^*$$

*Thus, given a pessimistic forecast, Zingtronics will minimize expected costs by subcontracting.

(b)

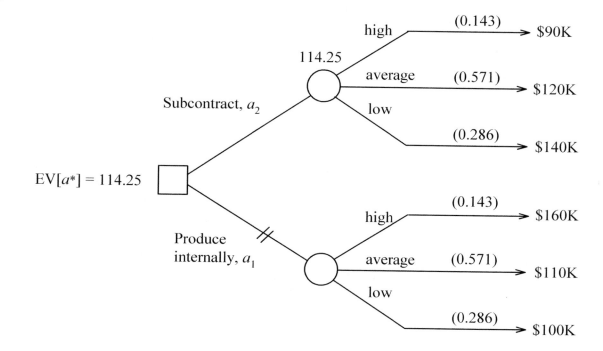

EV[a^*] = 114.25

(c) Bayes strategy

$$p(s_1 \,|\, f_1) = \frac{(0.1)(0.10)}{(0.1)(0.10)+(0.1)(0.60)+(0.5)(0.30)} = \frac{0.01}{0.01+0.06+0.15} = \frac{0.01}{0.22} = 0.045$$

$$p(s_2 \,|\, f_1) = \frac{(0.1)(0.60)}{0.22} = \frac{0.06}{0.22} = 0.273, \quad p(s_3 \,|\, f_1) = \frac{(0.5)(0.30)}{0.22} = 0.682$$

$$EV[a_1 \,|\, f_1] = (0.045)(140) + (0.273)(120) + (0.682)(90) = 100.44^*$$

$$EV[a_2 \,|\, f_1] = (0.045)(100) + (0.273)(110) + (0.682)(160) = 143.65$$

*The optimal action given an optimistic forecast, f_1, is to produce internally → a_1.

$$p(s_1 \,|\, f_2) = \frac{(0.3)(0.10)}{(0.3)(.10)+(0.7)(0.60)+(0.4)(0.30)} = \frac{0.03}{0.03+0.42+0.12} = 0.053$$

$$p(s_2 \,|\, f_2) = \frac{(0.7)(0.60)}{0.57} = 0.737, \quad p(s_3 \,|\, f_2) = \frac{0(.4)(0.30)}{0.57} = 0.210$$

$$EV[a_1 \,|\, f_2] = (0.053)(140) + (0.737)(120) + (0.210)(90) = 114.76^*$$

$$EV[a_2 \mid f_2] = (0.053)(100) + (0.737)(110) + (0.210)(160) = 119.97$$

*The optimal action given a normal forecast, f_2, is to produce internally → a_1.

In summary, the Bayes strategy is $f_1 \rightarrow a_1$, $f_2 \rightarrow a_1$, $f_3 \rightarrow a_2$.

(d) The maximum permissible fee must be smaller than the long-run *expected net benefits*, ENB, which is equal to the expected payoff without the forecast, $EV[a^*]$, minus the *long-term expected value*, LTEV, with the forecast.

$$LTEV = (0.22)(100.44) + (0.57)(114.76) + (0.21)(114.29) = 111.51$$

$$ENB = EV[a^*] - LTEV = 113 - 111.51 = 1.49$$

5.18   Let A, B, C, and D be four projects that are under consideration. The cost, probability of success, and benefits associated with each are tabulated below. Assume that projects A and B cannot both be undertaken due to resource limitations and that project D can begin only in the second year. Also assume that the analysis period is two years. Finally, let E denote the decision of not investing in any project after the first year.

Project	Cost	Prob. of success	Annual revenue if successful	Annual revenue if failure
A	$100,000	0.9	$75,000	$40,000
B	$100,000	0.8	$80,000	$35,000
C	$200,000	0.6	$200,000	$50,000
D	$100,000	0.7	$140,000	$60,000

The decision tree for the resultant problem is

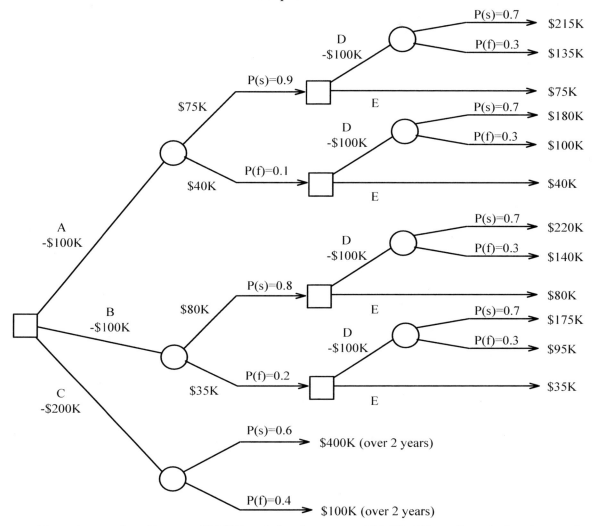

Note that project D costs $100K and that it returns $116K. Therefore, it dominates the do nothing decision E in each case.

5.19 (a)

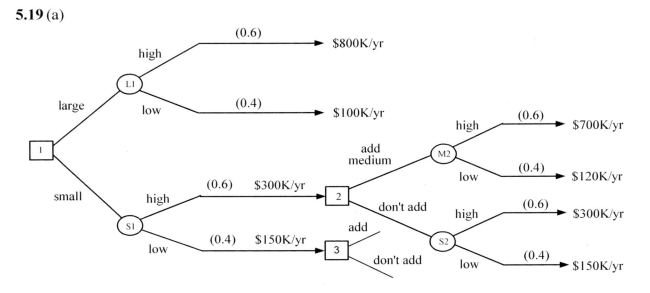

We begin calculations at decision point 2. If demand has been high, management faces the decision to add a medium size ship or continue to operate with the small one for the next 5 years.

EV[M2] = (0.6)(700,000)(5) + (0.4)(120,000)(5) = \$2,340,000 ← optimal action

EV[S2] = (0.6)(300,000)(5) + (0.4)(150,000)(5) = \$1,200,000

The same analysis holds for decision point 3.

(b) The above decision tree can be simplified now by including only the optimal action for the second phase.

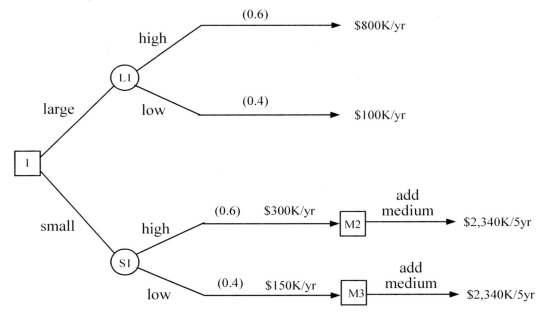

Calculating expected values for the simplified decision tree we have:

$$EV[L1] = (0.6)(800,000)(8) + (0.4)(100,000)(8) = \$4,160,000 \leftarrow \text{optimal action}$$

$$EV[S1] = (0.6)(300,000)(3) + (0.4)(150,000)(3) + 2,340,000$$
$$= 540,000 + 180,000 + 2,340,000 = \$3,060,000$$

(c) From (b) we see that Dream Cruises, Ltd. should buy the large ship now.

5.20 By discounting cash flows with $i = 12\%$ we have:

Stage 2:

$$EV[M2] = (0.6)(700,000(3.605) + (0.4)(120,000)(3.603)$$
$$= 1,514,100 + 173,040 = \$1,687,140$$

$$EV[S2] = (0.6)(300,000)(3.605) + (0.4)(120,000)(3.605)$$
$$= 648,900 + 173,040 = \$821,940$$

Stage 1:

$$EV[L1] = (0.6)(800,000)(4.968) + (0.4)(100,000)(4.968)$$
$$= 2,384,640 + 198,720 = \$2,583,360 \leftarrow \text{optimal action}$$

$$EV[S1] = (0.6)(300,000)(2.402) + (0.4)(150,000)(2.402) + (1,687,140)(0.7118)$$
$$= 432,360 + 144,120 + 1,200,906 = \$1,777,386$$

Conclusion: Following the same strategy identified in Exercise 5.19 and buy the large ship now.

5.21 $D1$ = use B-Team only, $D2$ = B-Team followed by A-Team
θ = percent of seams defective, $L(D, \theta)$ = material, labor, and rework costs

(a) For $D1$: $EV[L] = 400,000 + (1200)(1000)[(0.05)(0.3) + (0.10)(0.5) + (0.20)(0.2)]$
$= \$526,000$

For $D2$: $EV[L] = 530,000 + (1200)(1000)(0.01) = \$542,000$

When the criterion is to minimize expected cost, use B-Team. The expected cost is \$526K. Monetary values can be estimated for some aspects of environmental damage (e.g., water pollution due to oil spills), but the monetary approach breaks down when other aspects must be factored into the decision, such as reduction in wildlife. The use of a utility loss function can accommodate both aspects.

(b) D3 = inspect, D4 = don't inspect

X = Binomial random variable for number of inspected seams that turn out defective. (Refer to standard probability text for distribution values.)

	$f(X \mid \theta)$					
	$X = 0$	$X = 1$	$X = 2$	$X = 3$	$X = 4$	$X = 5$
$\theta = 0.05$	0.7733	0.2036	0.0214	0.0011	0.0000	0.0000
$\theta = 0.10$	0.5905	0.3280	0.0729	0.0081	0.0004	0.0000
$\theta = 0.20$	0.3277	0.4096	0.2048	0.0512	0.0064	0.0003

$$P(X = 0) = P(X{=}0 \mid \theta {=}0.05) \times P(\theta {=}0.05) + P(X{=}0 \mid \theta {=}0.05) \times P(\theta {=}0.05) +$$

$$P(X{=}0 \mid \theta {=}0.05) \times P(\theta {=}0.05)$$

$$= 0.7733 \times 0.3 + 0.5905 \times 0.5 + 0.3277 \times 0.2 = 0.5929$$

Similarly,

$$P(X = 1) = 0.2036 \times 0.3 + 0.3280 \times 0.5 + 0.4096 \times 0.2 = 0.307$$

$$P(X = 2) = 0.0214 \times 0.3 + 0.0729 \times 0.5 + 0.2048 \times 0.2 = 0.0838$$

$$P(X = 3) = 0.0011 \times 0.3 + 0.0081 \times 0.5 + 0.0512 \times 0.2 = 0.0147$$

$$P(X = 4) = 0.0000 \times 0.3 + 0.0004 \times 0.5 + 0.0064 \times 0.2 = 0.0015$$

$$P(X = 5) = 0.0000 \times 0.3 + 0.0000 \times 0.5 + 0.0003 \times 0.2 = 0.0001$$

Decision tree for
Exercise 5.21(b)

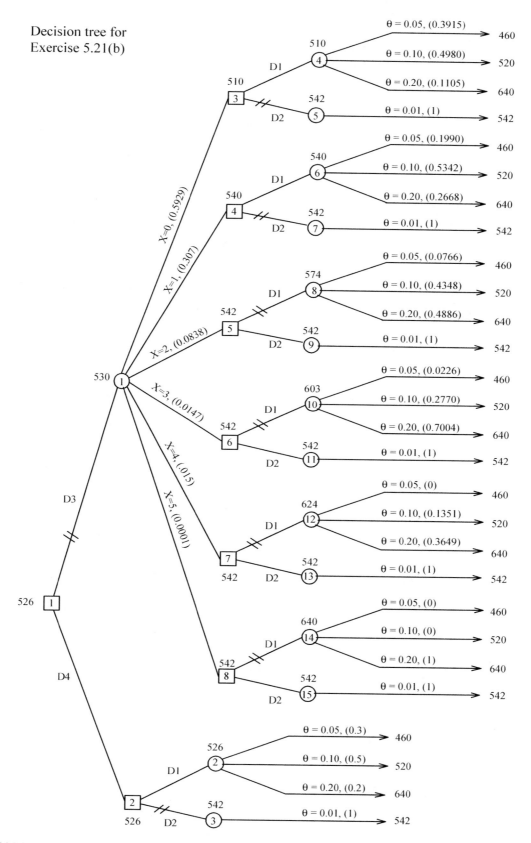

	$f(\theta \mid X)$		
	$\theta = 0.05$	$\theta = 0.10$	$\theta = 0.20$
$X = 0$	0.3915	0.4980	0.1105
$X = 1$	0.1990	0.5342	0.2668
$X = 2$	0.0766	0.4348	0.4886
$X = 3$	0.0226	0.2770	0.7004
$X = 4$	0.0000	0.1351	0.3649
$X = 5$	0.0000	0.0000	1.0000

Note that the probabilities in the decision tree following the chance forks 4, 6, 8, 10, 12 and 14 associated with D1 are posterior probabilities. Also, note that the $5,000 cost of experimentation must be added in at chance fork 1.

On average, we are $1,000 worse off by undertaking inspections. The optimal decision is to use the B-Team with no inspections. If the inspections were to cost less than $4,000, then they should be undertaken; in that case, the A-Team should be brought in whenever two or more defective seams are found.

5.22 (a) Opportunity loss matrix:

State, s	Don't Audit	Complete Audit
0.05	$0	$9,000
0.50	$0	$0
0.95	$19,000	$0

(b) Let D1 = no audit, D2 = complete audit, D3 = partial audit. The decision tree is given below. For conditional and joint probabilities, see (c) and (d). To save space, the branches in the tree that have an opportunity cost of zero are not shown.

(c) Let X = number of erroneous accounts in the sample. For a given value of s, X is a binomial random variable. The conditional probability matrix, $P(X \mid s)$, is

	$X = 0$	$X = 1$	$X = 2$	$X = 3$
$s = 0.05$	0.8574	0.1354	0.0071	0.0001
$s = 0.50$	0.1250	0.3750	0.3750	0.1250
$s = 0.95$	0.0001	0.0071	0.1354	0.8574

(d) Joint probabilities, $P(s, X)$:

	$X = 0$	$X = 1$	$X = 2$	$X = 3$
$s = 0.05$	0.1715	0.0271	0.0014	0.0000
$s = 0.50$	0.0875	0.2625	0.2625	0.0875
$s = 0.95$	0.0000	0.0007	0.0135	0.0875

$$P(X=0) = P(X=0|s=0.05) \times P(s=0.05) + P(X=0|s=0.50) \times P(s=0.50) +$$
$$P(X=0|s=0.95) \times P(s=0.95)$$
$$P(X=0) = 0.8574 \times 0.2 + 0.125 \times 0.7 + 0.001 \times 0.1 = 0.2591$$

Similarly,

$$P(X=1) = 0.1354 \times 0.2 + 0.375 \times 0.7 + 0.0071 \times 0.1 = 0.2903$$
$$P(X=2) = 0.0071 \times 0.2 + 0.375 \times 0.7 + 0.1354 \times 0.1 = 0.2775$$
$$P(X=3) = 0.0001 \times 0.2 + 0.125 \times 0.7 + 0.8574 \times 0.1 = 0.1732$$

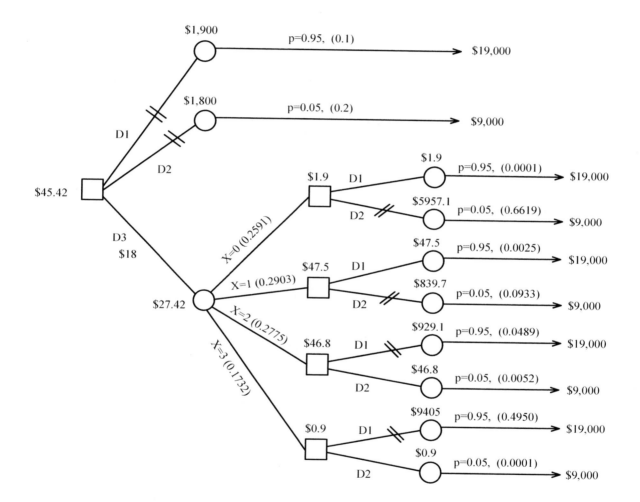

Posterior probabilities, $P(s|X)$:

	$s = 0.05$	$s = 0.50$	$s = 0.95$
$X = 0$	0.6619	0.3379	0.0001
$X = 1$	0.0933	0.9042	0.0025
$X = 2$	0.0052	0.9457	0.0489
$X = 3$	0.0001	0.5051	0.4950

(e) Partial auditing is better than a single audit plan.

1) From the decision tree we can see that the EOL when no audit is conducted is $1,900 whereas the EOL associated with a complete audit is $1,800. Therefore, the decision that minimizes EOL when no partial auditing is performed is D2 with corresponding value $1,800.

2) EMV under perfect information = $0 × 0.2 + $0 × 0.7 + $0 × 0.1 = $0. Note that when working with EOL, this value is always zero. Therefore, the EVPI = EOL.

3) EVSI = EVPI – EMV = $1,800 – $45.42 = $1,754.58.

4) Generally, the larger the sample size (number of partial audits) the more accurate the prediction of the proportion of errors in the accounts. However, each additional partial audit costs $6. At some point, the reduction in expected opportunity loss due to more accurate posterior probabilities would be offset by additional auditing costs. The optimal number of partial audits, n^*, could be determined by repeating the analysis for sample sizes of, say $n = 1, 2, 4, 5, 6$ and plotting optimal EMV against n. The value of n for which EMV is smallest would be the optimal sample size.

5.23

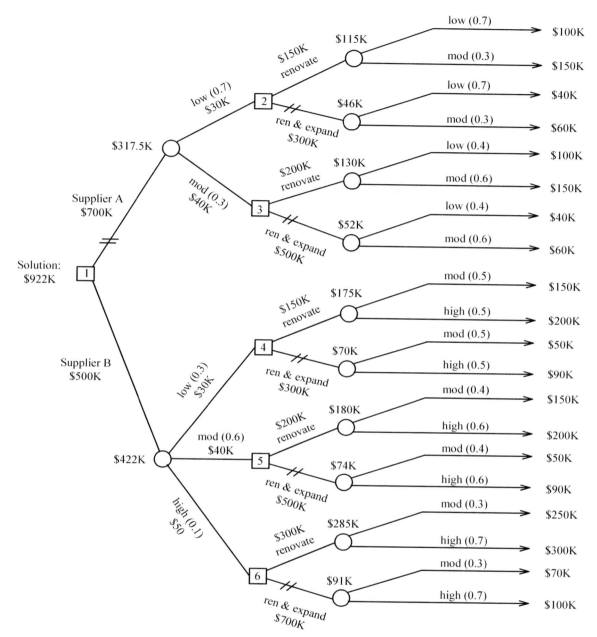

Node 6 = min{$700 + $91, $300K + $285K} = $585K

Node 5 = min{$500K + $74K, $200K + $180K} = $380K

Node 4 = min{$150K + $175K, $300K + $70K} = $325K

Node 3 = min{$200K + $130K, $500K + $52K} = $330K

Node 2 = min{$150K + $115K, $300K+$46K} = $265K

Node 1 = min{$700K + $317.5K, $500K + $422K} = $922K ← **Solution**

CHAPTER

6. MULTIPLE CRITERIA METHODS FOR EVALUATION

6.1 (a) Given below is a MAUT model to assist in the selection of computer-aided design (CAD) software. The three major criteria are the cost of the package, its capabilities, and ease of use. Costs consist of the initial cost of the software plus the cost of annual upgrades provided by the vendor. The capability of the software determines its usefulness to the designer. The design process can be greatly accelerated if the software provides a large library of solutions and tools for standard design problems. In addition, the software needs to be computationally efficient. Productivity is related directly to user friendliness. A good graphical user interface together with detailed documentation and responsive customer support help designers make better use of the software.

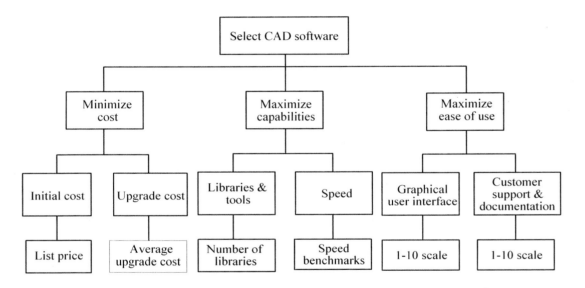

(b) An AHP model for the problem might take the following form.

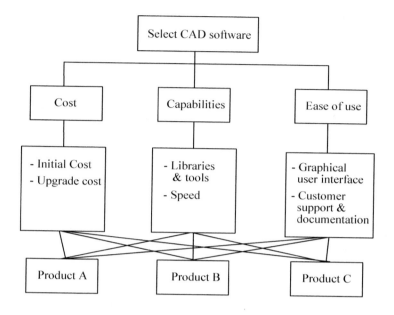

Typically, the decision makers for CAD software purchases are VLSI design engineers and project managers. The design engineers would probably prefer top-of-the-line software with sophisticated user interfaces and extensive options regardless of cost. In contrast, project managers may opt for software that satisfies the technical requirements at a minimum cost.

6.2

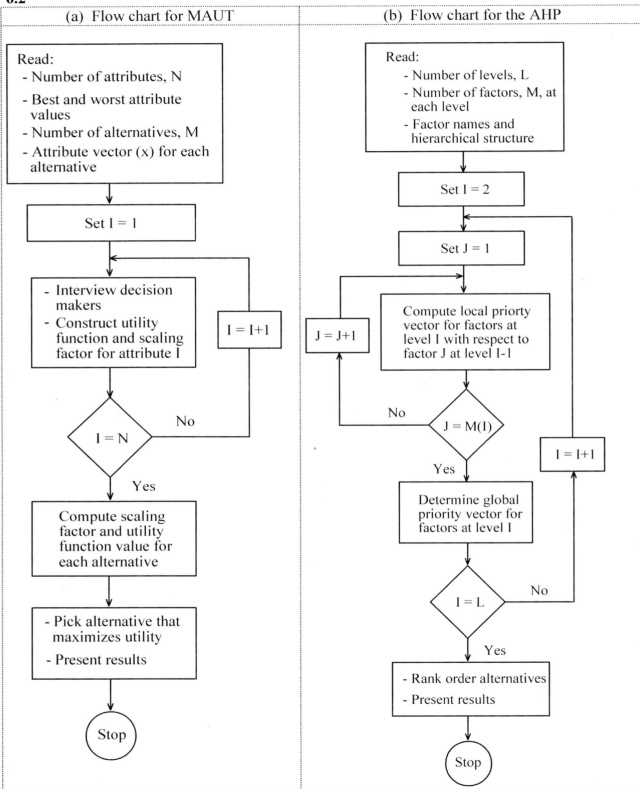

| (a) Flow chart for MAUT | (b) Flow chart for the AHP |

6.3 Major factors to be considered in selecting a graduate program might include costs, quality of education, and quality of life. Costs can be broken down by tuition/fees and living expenses. Quality of education factors include research interests of the faculty, course offerings, school reputation, and the infrastructure; e.g., library and computing facilities. Under quality of life we consider the housing market and the recreational facilities.

MAUT model

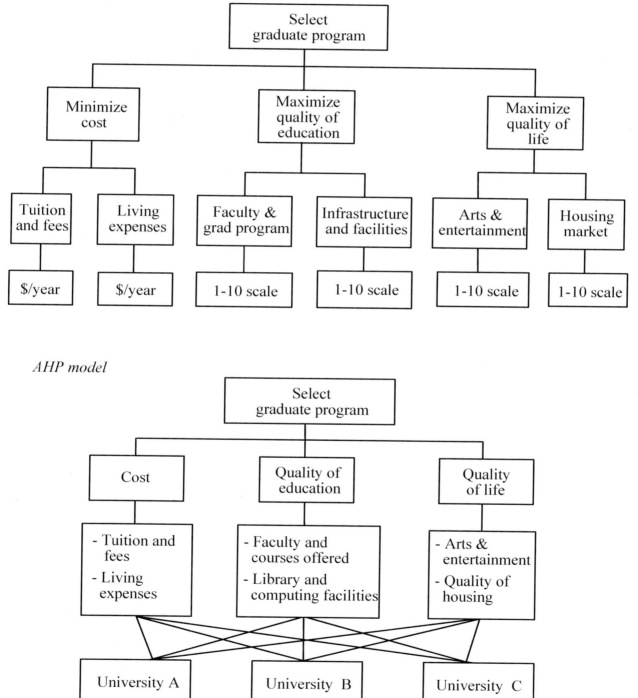

AHP model

6.4 Considering only major factors, one possible cost objective hierarchy follows.

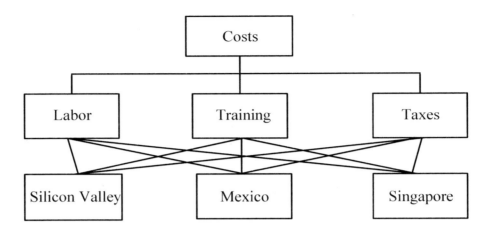

The comparison matrix for the three major factors with respect to the cost objective is presented in the table below, along with the computations.

Criteria	1	2	3	Priorities	Output parameters
1. Labor	1	7	7	0.766	$\lambda_{max} = 3.316$
2. Training	1/7	1	3	0.158	CI = 0.068
3. Taxes	1/7	1/3	1	0.076	CR = 0.117

After performing the pairwise comparisons for the three alternatives with respect to each of the cost factors, the following global weights were obtained:

Silicon Valley = 0.145, Mexico = 0.588, Singapore = 0.268

Simplified benefit objective hierarchy

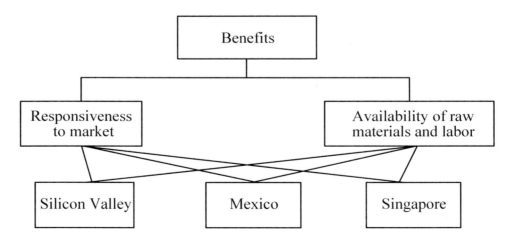

Comparison matrix and results

Criteria	1	2	Priorities	Output parameters
1. Responsiveness	1	5	0.833	$\lambda_{max} = 2$
2. Raw materials	1/5	1	0.167	$CI = CR = 0.0$

Global weights for the 3 alternatives are:

Silicon Valley = 0.742, Mexico = 0.167, Singapore = 0.091

The benefit-cost ratio analysis indicates that Silicon Valley is the best choice for locating the new plant.

Alternative	B/C ratio	Ranking
Silicon Valley	5.117	1
Mexico	3.521	2
Singapore	2.945	3

6.5 A combined hierarchical model for the location problem is given below. We define a 1-10 qualitative scale for each attribute.

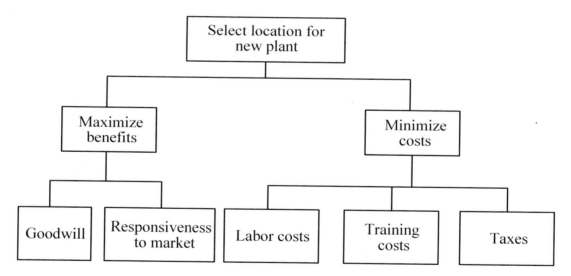

Utility functions for the attributes are constructed by interviewing the decision maker. Let x_1, x_2, x_3, x_4, and x_5 correspond to the attributes goodwill, responsiveness, labor costs, training costs, and taxes, respectively, and assume that lottery question responses for the ith attribute produced utility function $U(x_i)$ and scaling constant k_i as follows:

$U(x_i)$	Attribute range				
	x_1	x_2	x_3	x_4	x_5
0.00	1	1	1	1	1
0.25	4	5	6	5	6
0.50	7	6	7	6	7
0.75	8	7	8	7	8
1.00	10	10	10	10	10
k_i	0.7	0.6	0.6	0.2	0.1

For these data, the master scaling constant k is approximately -0.964. The decision maker's assessment on the 1-10 scale for each attribute for each of the three locations is given in the next table.

Location	Decision maker's assessments				
	x_1	x_2	x_3	x_4	x_5
Silicon Valley	10	8	2	9	4
Mexico	7	6	9	2	8
Singapore	3	7	8	8	7

Using linear interpolation to find the corresponding utility function values and plugging the results into the multiplicative model (6.1a) yields the following values for the three alternatives.

U(Silicon Valley) = 0.7479, U(Mexico) = 0.8691, U(Singapore) = 0.9110

Thus, MAUT indicates that the best location for the new plant is Singapore.

6.6 A hierarchical model for selecting a political candidate is given below.

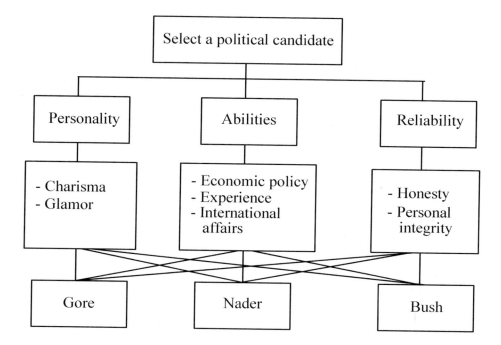

Depending on who the decision maker is, we would get a first level matrix that looked something like the following.

Criteria	1	2	3	Priorities	Output parameters
1. Personality	1	0.143	0.333	0.081	$\lambda_{max} = 3.065$
2. Abilities	7	1	5	0.731	CI = 0.033
3. Reliability	3	0.2	1	0.188	CR = 0.056

In the next step of a top-down approach, pairwise comparisons would be made between the subcriteria with respect to major criteria above them. We omit this step and simply compare the candidates with respect to the three major criteria. The comparison matrices and the local weights are given below.

Personality	Gore	Nader	Bush	Priorities	Output parameters
Gore	1	5	0.333	0.297	$\lambda_{max} = 3.136$
Nader	0.2	1	0.2	0.068	CI = 0.068
Bush	3	5	1	0.618	CR = 0.117

Abilities	Gore	Nader	Bush	Priorities	Output parameters
Gore	1	7	3	0.649	$\lambda_{max} = 3.065$
Nader	0.143	1	0.2	0.072	CI = 0.032
Bush	0.333	5	1	0.279	CR = 0.056

Reliability	Gore	Nader	Bush	Priorities	Output parameters
Gore	1	3	3	0.584	$\lambda_{max} = 3.136$
Nader	0.333	1	0.333	0.135	CI = 0.068
Bush	0.333	3	1	0.281	CR = 0.117

For this particular decision maker, the global weights for the 3 alternatives are Bush = 0.307, Gore = 0.608, Nader = 0.085, implying that Gore is the preferred candidate.

6.7 The preference curve for attribute A, for example, can be constructed by asking the decision maker a series of lottery questions of the form "For attribute A, what certain outcome, x_A, would be equally desirable as realizing the highest outcome with probability p and the lowest outcome with probability $1 - p$?" The values of p for which the question was asked to the decision maker along with his responses are tabulated below. These values are used to approximate the utility curve for attribute A; that is, $U(x_A) = p$.

Prob (p)	0.0	0.2	0.4	0.6	0.8	1.0
x_A	1,000	500	300	200	100	0

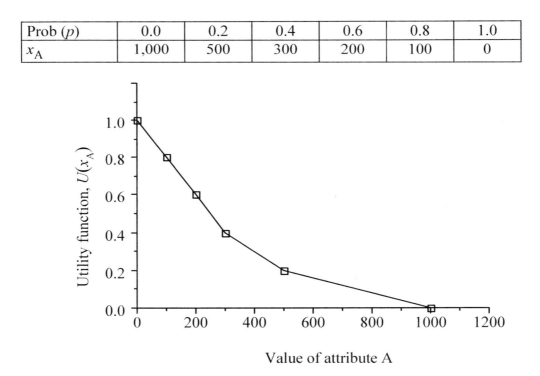

Similarly, the utility curves for other attributes are approximated using the following tables.

Prob (p)	0.0	0.3	0.6	1.0
x_B	poor	good	very good	excellent
x_C	poor	good	very good	excellent

Prob (p)	0.0	0.4	0.6	0.8	1.0
x_D	10,000	7,500	5,000	2,500	0

Prob (p)	0.0	0.1	0.3	0.5	0.6	0.8	1.0
x_E	150,000	125,000	100,000	75,000	50,000	25,000	10,000

The scaling factors for various attributes were found to be:

Attribute	Scaling factor, k_i	Normalized k_i
A	0.2	0.09
B	0.3	0.13
C	0.6	0.26
D	0.5	0.22
E	0.7	0.3

Using the additive model, values of the utility function for the three alternatives are:

U(Area 1) = 0.567, U(Area 2) = 0.561, U(Area 3) = 0.486, so the best choice is Area 1.

6.8 An objective hierarchy for evaluating capital development and expansion projects in the electric utilities industry would have at least two major components. The first would address the environmental impacts; the second would consider the benefits from a multiplicity of viewpoints, including technology, the rate payers, the community, and financial markets. In the hierarchy below numbers 1 and 2 refer to major objectives; single decimal numbers (e.g., 1.1 - 1.3) refer to subobjectives for a given major objective; double decimal numbers (e.g., 2.1.1 - 2.1.5) refer to components of subobjectives. Attributes are in parentheses. At the lowest level, numbering could refer to either objectives or attributes (e.g., objective 2.1.1 and attribute 2.1.1).

1. Environmental considerations

   1.1 Air emissions
   - 1.1.1 Sulfur oxides (lbs/MWh)
   - 1.1.2 Nitrogen oxides (lbs/MWh)
   - 1.1.3 Carbon dioxide (lbs/MWh)
   - 1.1.4 Particulates (lbs/MWh)

   1.2 Water effects
   - 1.2.1 Cooling water flow (annual intake as % of lake volume)
   - 1.2.2 Fish protection (qualitative scale: 0-1)
   - 1.2.3 NYS quality classification of receiving water (qualitative scale: 0-1)

   1.3 Land effects
   - 1.3.1 Acreage required (acres/MW)
   - 1.3.2 Terrestrial (current perceived value of land; qualitative scale: 0-1)
   - 1.3.3 Visual aesthetics (qualitative scale: 0-1)
   - 1.3.4 Transmission (qualitative scale based on mode: 0-1)
   - 1.3.5 Noise (L_{eq} – background L_{90})
   - 1.3.6 Solid waste disposal (lbs/MWh)
   - 1.3.7 Fuel delivery (qualitative scale based on mode: 0-1)
   - 1.3.8 Location (km from receptor area)

2. Benefits

   2.1 Rate payers
   - 2.1.1 Residential customer fees (change in $/KWh)
   - 2.1.2 Commercial customer fees (change in $/KWh)
   - 2.1.3 Quality of service (expected outages/year, expected duration of outages)

   2.2 Community
   - 2.2.1 Contribution to economic development (jobs created)
   - 2.2.2 Public health and safety (person-years of disability, lost work time, life lost)
   - 2.2.3 Perception as public citizen (qualitative scale: 0-1)
   - 2.2.4 Impact on other businesses ($)

   2.3 Technology
   - 2.3.1 Potential for expansion (qualitative scale: 0-1)
   - 2.3.2 Ease of operations (qualitative scale: 0-1)
   - 2.3.3 Internal health and safety (person-years of disability, lost work time, life lost)
   - 2.3.4 Industry leadership (qualitative scale: 0-1)
   - 2.3.5 Development risks (cost overruns, schedule overruns)

When considering projects that have substantial costs and risks, it would be appropriate to introduce an additional major objective that addressed the economics directly. Subobjectives might include initial costs, recurrent costs, and productivity improvements.

6.9 (a) In the strategic objectives hierarchy below[†] the same numbering scheme introduced in Exercise 6.8 is used.

1. Maximize contribution to economic development

    1.1 Minimize cost of electricity use (mills per kilowatt-hour in dollars)
    1.2 Maximize funds transferred to government (annualized dividend payable)
    1.3 Minimize economic implications of resource losses (cost of resource losses in dollars)

2. Act consistently with the public's environmental values concerning

    2.1 Local environmental impacts
        2.1.1 To flora (hectares of mature forest lost)
        2.1.2 To fauna (hectares of wildlife habitat lost of Spatzizi Plateau quality)
        2.1.3 To wildlife ecosystems (hectares of wilderness lost of the Stikine Valley quality)
        2.1.4 To limit recreational use (hectares of high quality recreational land lost)
        2.1.5 To aesthetics (annual person-years viewing high voltage transmission lines)

    2.2 Global impacts (generation capacity in megawatts that results in "fossil fuel" pollution)

3. Minimize detrimental health and safety impacts

    3.1 To the public
        3.1.1. Mortality (public person-years of life lost)
        3.1.2. Morbidity (public person-years of disability equal in severity to that causing employee lost work time)

    3.2 To employees
        3.2.1 Mortality (employee person-years of life lost)
        3.2.2 Morbidity (employee person-years of lost work time)

4. Promote equitable business arrangements

    4.1 Equitable pricing to different customers (constructed scale)
    4.2 Equitable compensation for concentrated local impacts (number of individuals that feel they are inequitably treated)

5. Maximize quality of service

    5.1 To small customers
        5.1.1 Minimize outages (expected number of annual outages to a small customer)
        5.1.2 Minimize duration of outages (average hours of outage per incident to small customers)

[†] Taken from R. L. Keeney and T. L. McDaniels, "Value-Focused Thinking about Strategic Decisions at BC Hydro," *Interfaces,* Vol. 22, No. 6, pp. 94-109 (1992).

    5.2 To large customers
        5.2.1   Minimize outages (expected number of annual outages to a large customer)
        5.2.2   Minimize duration of outages (average hours of outage per incidence to large customers)

    5.3 Improve new service (elapsed time until new service is installed)
    5.4 Improve response to telephone inquiries (time until person answers the telephone)

6. Be recognized as public service oriented (constructed scale)

    6.1 Donations to charities (dollar value of gifts)
    6.2 Support of community activities
        6.2.1   Time off for workers (person-hours per year)
        6.2.2   Contributions in facilities, expertise, and cash (dollar equivalent)

6.9 (b) Possible measures for attributes

No.	Objective (attribute)	Worst level	Best level
1.1	Average cost of energy from new sources at grid (mills / KWh)	55	35
1.2	Annualized dividend payable (dollars in millions)	0	$200
1.3	Economic cost of resource losses (dollars in millions)	$20	0
2.1.1	Flora (hectares of mature forest)	10,000	0
2.1.2	Fauna (hectares of wildlife habitat-Spatzizi Plateau quality)	10,000	0
2.1.3	Wilderness ecosystem (hectares of wilderness loss-Stikine Valley quality)	10,000	0
2.1.4	Recreation (hectares of recreational land lost-provincial park quality)	10,000	0
2.1.5	Aesthetic (annual person-years viewing high voltage transmission line in quality terrain)	500,000	0
2.2	Global environmental impact (megawatts of fossil pollutants)	1,000	0
3.1.1	Public mortality (annual person-years of life lost)	100	0
3.1.2	Public morbidity (annual person-years "severe" disability)	1,000	0
3.2.1	Worker mortality (annual person-years life lost)	100	0
3.2.2	Worker morbidity (annual person-years lost work time)	1,000	0
4.1	Equitable pricing (constructed scale)	0.5	0
4.2	Equitable compensation (annual average number of individuals who suffer significant impact, such as property loss, felt to be inequitably treated)	500	0
5.1.1	Small customer outages (annual number / customer)	2	0
5.1.2	Small customer outage duration (hours / outage)	24	0
5.2.1	Large customer outages (annual number / customer)	2	0
5.2.2	Large customer outage duration (hours / outage)	24	0
5.3	New service (hook up time in work days)	20	1
5.4	Inquiries (time until personal response in minutes)	1	0
6.1	Donations to charities (dollar value of gifts)	0	$2M
6.2.1	Time off for workers (person-hours per year)	0	100,000
6.2.1	Contributions in facilities, expertise, and cash (dollar equivalent)	0	$1M

6.10 (a) Assume the following attribute rankings and scores.

		Points				
	Rank	0	1	2	3	4
Aesthetics	1	1-2	3-4	5-6	7-8	9-10
Performance	2	poor	fair	good	very good	excellent
Prices	3	> 25,000	20,001-25,000	15,001-20,000	10,001-15,000	≤ 10,000
Fuel type	4		diesel	gasoline		
Gas (mpg)	5	< 20	20-24	25-29	30-34	≥ 35
Service	6	poor	fair	Good	very good	Excellent
Head room	7	poor	fair	good	very good	excellent
Passengers	8	2	4	6	8	10
Storage	9	poor	fair	good	very good	excellent
Stereo	10	poor	fair	good	very good	excellent

1. Uniform weights

Attribute	Relative weight	Domestic Score	Factor score	European Score	Factor score	Japanese Score	Factor score
Aesthetics	0.1	2	0.2	3	0.3	4	0.4
Performance	0.1	1	0.1	3	0.3	3	0.3
Prices	0.1	4	0.4	3	0.3	3	0.3
Fuel type	0.1	2	0.2	1	0.1	2	0.2
Gas (mpg)	0.1	2	0.2	3	0.3	4	0.4
Service	0.1	4	0.4	3	0.3	2	0.2
Head room	0.1	4	0.4	3	0.3	0	0.0
Passengers	0.1	1	0.1	2	0.2	1	0.1
Storage	0.1	3	0.3	4	0.4	0	0.0
Stereo	0.1	0	0.0	2	0.2	4	0.4
Total	1.0		2.3		2.7		2.3

Decision: Select European car.

2. Rank sum weights

	Rank	Relative weight	Domestic		European		Japanese	
			Score	Factor score	Score	Factor score	Score	Factor score
Aesthetics	1	0.18	2	0.36	3	0.54	4	0.72
Performance	2	0.16	1	0.16	3	0.48	3	0.48
Prices	3	0.15	4	0.6	3	0.45	3	0.45
Fuel type	4	0.13	2	0.26	1	0.13	2	0.26
Gas (mpg)	5	0.11	2	0.22	3	0.33	4	0.44
Service	6	0.09	4	0.36	3	0.27	2	0.18
Head room	7	0.07	4	0.28	3	0.21	0	0.00
Passengers	8	0.05	1	0.05	2	0.10	1	0.05
Storage	9	0.04	3	0.12	4	0.16	0	0.00
Stereo	10	0.02	0	0.00	2	0.04	4	0.08
Total		1.00		2.41		2.71		2.66

Decision: Select European car

3. Rank reciprocal weights

Attribute	Rank	Relative weight	Domestic		European		Japanese	
			Score	Factor score	Score	Factor score	Score	Factor score
Aesthetics	1	0.34	2	0.68	3	1.02	4	1.36
Performance	2	0.17	1	0.17	3	0.51	3	0.51
Prices	3	0.11	4	0.44	3	0.33	3	0.33
Fuel type	4	0.09	2	0.18	1	0.09	2	0.18
Gas (mpg)	5	0.07	2	0.14	3	0.21	4	0.28
Service	6	0.06	4	0.24	3	0.18	2	0.12
Head room	7	0.05	4	0.2	3	0.15	0	0.00
Passengers	8	0.04	1	0.04	2	0.08	1	0.04
Storage	9	0.04	3	0.12	4	0.16	0	0.00
Stereo	10	0.03	0	0.00	2	0.06	4	0.12
Total		1.00		2.21		2.79		2.94

Decision: Select Japanese car

6.11 An aspiration-level model was developed by V. Lotfi, T. Stewart, and S. Zionts and is discussed in their paper "An Aspiration-Level Interactive Model (AIM) for Multiple Criteria Decision Making," *Computers & Operations Research*, Vol. 19, No. 7, (1992) pp. 671-681. The flow diagram below highlights the logic of the methodology.

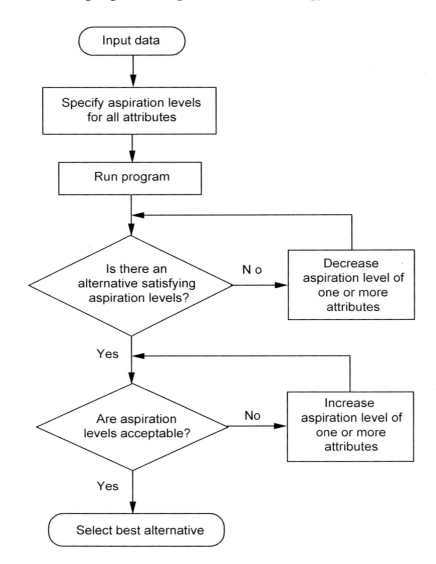

Using the AIM program, the aspirations levels of each objective were set to their median values with respect to the three alternatives. For fuel type, it was assumed that gasoline is preferred to diesel. In addition, a 0-4 score was used to quantify the qualitative choices poor through excellent and 0-1 scale was used to quantify aesthetics. No alternative was dominant but the Japanese car appeared to be the best compromise. Next, the aspirations levels were varied to determine how much each would have to change so that a particular alternative would be selected. The results are presented in the following table.

Columns: Case, Price ($k), Gas (mpg), Fuel type, Aesthetics, Passengers, Performance, Service, Stereo, Head room, Store space, C

Row 1: 1, 10.3, 30, Gasoline, 0.7, 4, very good, very good, good, very good, very good, Japanese
Row 2: 2, 12.6, 25, Diesel, 0.5, 4, fair, good, poor, poor, poor, Domestic
Row 3: 3, 8.1, 25, Gasoline, 0.5, 4, fair, excel, poor, excel, very good, Domestic
Row 4: 4, 12.6, 30, Diesel, 0.7, 4, very good, good, good, poor, poor, Japanese
Row 5: 5, 10.3, 35, Gasoline, 0.9, 4, very good, good, excel, poor, poor, Japanese
Row 6: 6, 12.6, 30, Diesel, 0.7, 4, very good, very good, good, very good, very good, European
Row 7: 7, 12.6, 30, Diesel, 0.7, 6, very good, very good, good, very good, excel, European

Aspiration Levels and Corresponding Choices

Case	Price ($k)	Gas (mpg)	Fuel type	Aesthetics	Passengers	Performance	Service	Stereo	Head room	Store space	C
1	10.3	30	Gasoline	0.7	4	very good	very good	good	very good	very good	Japanese
2	12.6	25	Diesel	0.5	4	fair	good	poor	poor	poor	Domestic
3	8.1	25	Gasoline	0.5	4	fair	excel	poor	excel	very good	Domestic
4	12.6	30	Diesel	0.7	4	very good	good	good	poor	poor	Japanese
5	10.3	35	Gasoline	0.9	4	very good	good	excel	poor	poor	Japanese
6	12.6	30	Diesel	0.7	4	very good	very good	good	very good	very good	European
7	12.6	30	Diesel	0.7	6	very good	very good	good	very good	excel	European

Case description:

1. Baseline: aspiration levels are set to the median value of the three alternatives. None of the alternatives satisfies these aspiration levels but the Japanese car comes closest.
2. Aspiration levels are the lowest possible for domestic car to be selected.
3. Aspiration levels are the highest possible for domestic car to be selected.
4. Aspiration levels are the lowest possible for Japanese car to be selected.
5. Aspiration levels are the highest possible for Japanese car to be selected.
6. Aspiration levels are the lowest possible for European car to be selected.
7. Aspiration levels are the highest possible for European car to be selected.

CHAPTER

7. SCOPE AND ORGANIZATIONAL STRUCTURE OF A PROJECT

7.1   Consider a joint venture between the Business School and the School of Medicine aimed at the development of a new degree program in the management of health services. Because both participants are at the same level in the university hierarchy, it makes sense to have two project coordinators, one from each school. As is common in education, both schools have a functional structure.

For project likes this, the organizational structure should be a weak matrix in which the two coordinators call on resources (e.g., professors, laboratories) from the different functional areas in their corresponding school to develop the new program. Both will be equally responsible for the definition of the curriculum, the assessment of needs, the integration of the two disciplines, the acquisition of new resources, and the implementation of the program.

7.2   *A New Solar Heater Project*

Assuming that the project is performed by a functional organization with a strong engineering department, the project manager will be an engineer with some managerial experience (with an MBA, if possible). Two engineers will be assigned to the project full time to perform most of the work. The first will be responsible for all R&D activities including the development of a prototype. The second will be responsible for the transition from development to production.

Both engineers will report to a senior project manager responsible for scheduling, budgeting and integration problems. The work breakdown structure will follow a similar line as shown below.

WBS

1.   Solar Heater Project
     1.1   R&D Management
            1.1.1   Electrical components
            1.1.2   Mechanical components
            1.1.3   Computer hardware
            1.1.3   Computer software
            1.1.4   Integration of design
            1.1.5   Quality Control
            1.1.6   Budgeting of R&D activities
            1.1.6   Scheduling of R&D activities
            1.1.7   Configuration management
            1.1.8   Logistics
            1.1.9   Prototype

     1.2   Transition to Production

1.2.1   Production and assembly of electrical parts
1.2.2   Production and assembly of mechanical parts
1.2.3   Assembly of computer control
1.2.4   Software installation and integration
1.2.5   Integration of mechanical, electrical and logic components
1.2.6   Quality control and quality assurance plans
1.2.7   Preparation of training material for assembly workers
1.2.8   Inventory control, production scheduling
1.2.9   Facility design

7.3   *Emergency Health Care Unit*

Assuming that the hospital has a functional structure, which is most often the case, the emergency health care unit draws on the resources of the various departments as needed. The proposed organizational structure is thus based on the idea teams, which are formed on an ad-hoc for each patient. In particular, the teams are assigned by the head resident and consist of one or more doctors, one or more nurses, and perhaps medical students.

The emergency unit is related to other units in the following ways: (1) patients are referred to other areas when the emergency has passed (sent to ICU, recovery, surgery, released, etc.); (2) shared administrative department (admissions, billing). The OBS is shown in the figure below.

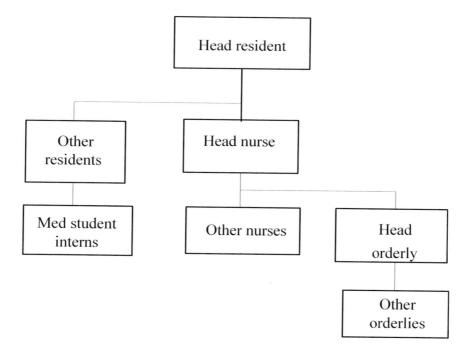

7.4 *Construction Project.* The proposed WBS is based on the type of work to be performed, which has a high correlation with the stage in the project life cycle.

1. Construction Project
   1.1 Design
   1.2 Foundation
   1.3 Walls and Floor
   1.4 Plumbing and Electricity
   1.5 Finish
   1.6 Landscaping
   1.7 Project Management
   1.8 Logistics

7.5 Consider the development of a new electric car by an auto manufacturer and a manufacturer of high-capacity batteries.

(a) The WBS
   1. New Electric Car
      1.1 Car development
         1.1.1 Body
            1.1.1.1 Frame
            1.1.1.2 Fixed parts
            1.1.1.3 Doors
            1.1.1.4 Interior
         1.1.2 Gear train
            1.1.2.1 Motor
            1.1.2.2 Transmission
            1.1.2.3 Wheels and axles
         1.1.3 Integration
            1.1.3.1 Of body
            1.1.3.2 Of gear train
            1.1.3.3 Of body and gear train
      1.2 Battery development
         1.2.1 Mechanical development
            1.2.1.1 Housing
            1.2.2.2 Connections
         1.2.2 Chemical development
            1.2.2.1 Solid components
            1.2.2.2 Fluids used in battery
      1.3 Integration of Battery and Body
         1.3.1 Mechanical integration
         1.3.2 Electrical integration
      1.4 Project management
         1.4.1 Scheduling
            1.4.1.1 Development of activity network
            1.4.1.2 Computer runs and development of schedules
         1.4.2 Project control

(b) The OBS
 1. Project management
  1.1 Car manufacturer
   1.1.1 Mechanical engineering
   1.1.2 Electrical engineering
   1.1.3 Manufacturing engineering
  1.2 Battery manufacturer
   1.2.1 Chemical engineering
   1.2.2 Mechanical engineering
   1.2.3 Manufacturing engineering
  1.3 Integration and quality control
   1.3.1 Car integration
   1.3.2 Quality control
  1.4 Project management and logistics
   1.4.1 Project management
   1.4.2 Contract management
   1.4.3 Purchasing
   1.4.4 Contracts

(c) A typical work package relates a lower level WBS element to a lower OBS element. For example, the following can be thought of as a work package can be thought

WBS	OBS
1.1.1.1	1.1.1
1.1.2.1	1.1.2
1.1.3.1	1.3.2

7.6 (a) WBS for the development of a new undergraduate program in Electrical Engineering

 1. EE Undergraduate Program
  1.1 Basic courses
   1.1.1 Mathematics
   1.1.2 Physics
   1.1.3 Chemistry
   1.1.4 Computer Science
   1.1.5 English and Arts
  1.2 General engineering
   1.2.1 Thermodynamics
   1.2.2 Materials
   1.2.3 Computer aided design and drafting
   1.2.4 Control
  1.3 Electrical engineering
   1.3.1 Components
    1.3.1.1 Analog
    1.3.1.2 Digital
   1.3.2 Circuits

1.3.2.1 Analog
1.3.2.2 Digital
1.4 Advanced engineering
1.4.1 Computer systems
1.4.2 High frequent and electro-optics
1.4.2 Numerical control
1.5 Upper level support courses
1.5.1 Quality and reliability
1.5.2 Project management
1.5.2.1 R&D projects
1.5.2.2 Manufacturing projects

(b) OBS. Because the new program contains courses from other schools e.g., sciences, liberal arts) as well as EE, a committee should be formed to oversee its development. The committee should be chaired by a senior EE faculty and be composed of members from all the different schools that contribute to the curriculum. The members will draw on their individual knowledge to develop courses that relate to their area of expertise, perhaps with help from other faculty in their home departments.

7.7 The project we consider is to install a new computer catalog in a downtown library, replacing the existing card catalog. In the LRC both the constructor and the client play an important role. The head librarian in the client organization has the responsibility to approve plans technical specifications of the system, for example, while the constructor has the responsibility to implement those plans within the agreed upon budget and schedule.

(a) WBS

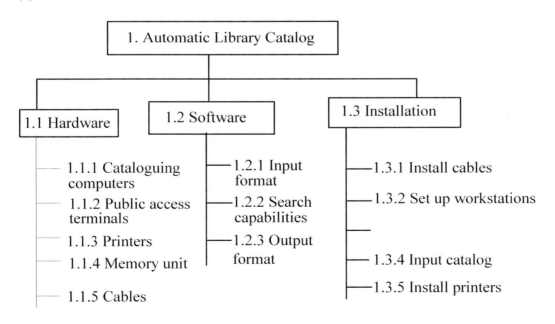

(b.1) Client OBS

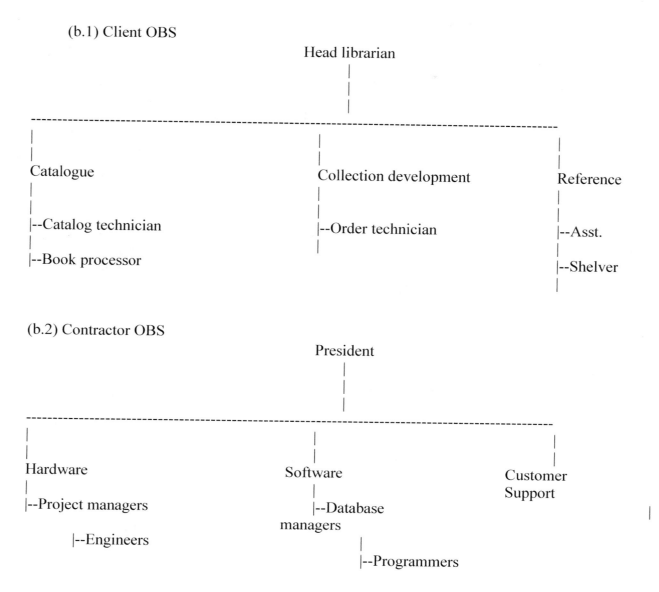

(b.2) Contractor OBS

7.8 The first OBS is based on product lines, each line having a corresponding organizational unit responsible for the development, manufacturing, distribution and service of its products. The development of new generations, as well as logistic support for each product type, are handled by the same organizational unit. This provides an advantage because management and the technical staff can concentrate their efforts on a small number of products. However, the duplication of functions for different product lines leads to the inefficient use of resources.

The second OBS is a traditional functional organization. Units such as engineering, marketing, and manufacturing are responsible for the corresponding activities on all product lines. This structure makes better use of resources and information since they are shared among all products lines; however, there is no focal point for each product type so customer service may suffer as a result.

7.9 Activity I: *A Family White Water Rafting Trip*

On this outing, my family was the customer and the rafting company organizing the trip was the contractor. The tour guide served as the "project manager" for the contractor, and escorted us from the pickup point to the end of the river. Using the resources of the company, he developed the schedule, planned the logistics (food, transportation), and was responsible for safety. In fact, he was the only point of contact we had with the company after making the reservations and paying the fees.

Activity II: *Going to a Restaurant*

In this activity, the customer plays a role in the planning phase (selecting from the menu) the waiter serves as a communication channel and provide material handling services, while the kitchen provide cooking services. The owner of the restaurant is responsibility for quality control, customer relations, and overall management.

7.10 Many government agencies do not operate in an efficient manner, have cumbersome decision-making processes, and are slow to react to request or mandates due to complex organizational structures. The major problems are lack of motivation and a poor attitude toward customers stemming primarily from the monopoly that governments have on most services they provide. Solutions include reducing the role of government, minimizing government involvement in supplying services, providing more incentives and penalties for the work force, streamlining processes, and giving individuals more responsibility. In the last few years, many government agencies have outsourced a portion of their charge to private firms. This includes internal functions like information and janitorial services as well as external functions like call centers.

7.11 Setting up a new restaurant.

(a) The code consists of four fields, each containing one or more digits, depending on the level of activity. The leftmost digit represents the first level of the WBS and so on, up to the fourth level. The following partial solution demonstrates a possible code:

Level	Work content	Code number
1	Project – new restaurant	1 _ _ _
2	Specification of needs	1 1 _ _
3	Study needs	1 1 1 _
3	Restaurant survey	1 1 2 _
3	Possible food	1 1 3 _
3	Possible services	1 1 4 _
.		
.		
.		
2	Labor preparation	1 5 _ _
3	Labor preparation - service	1 5 1 _
4	Labor preparation – service – req'ts	1 5 1 1
4	Labor preparation – service – training	1 5 1 2

(b) Any project that has similar work content can use the coding scheme developed above, a portion of it, or an expanded version of it. Examples might be a chain of new restaurants or the opening of a service center such as automotive repair shop. Both cases would closely parallel the WBS presented in Fig. 7.11.

(c) In a construction project such as building or a bridge, the product design and the process design should concentrate on construction related issues. These might include the types of material used, the testing and curing processes, the support subsystems (scaffolding), and equipment rentals.

7.12 Continuation of the restaurant project in Exercise 7.11.

(a) The matrix organization as depicted in the following diagram is one possible OBS.

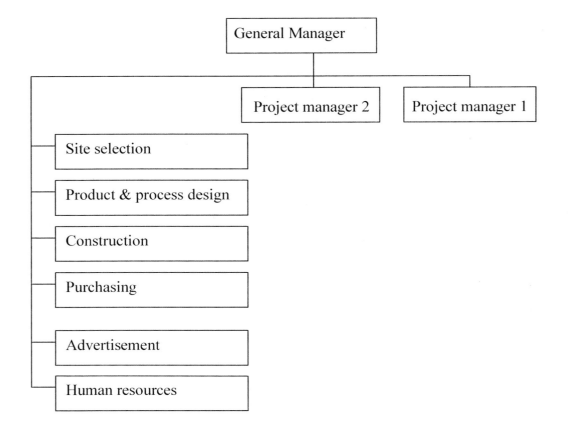

(b) The work package "restaurant survey" will be assigned to the "site selection" department. The work package "design cold dishes" will be assigned to the "product and process design" department. The work package "electricity" will be assigned to the construction department.

(c) The "restaurant survey" package should be coordinated with the "product and process design" department to determine potential names that don't conflict with known competitors. The "design cold dishes" package should be coordinated with the "construction" department to ensure that freezing requirements are addressed. The "electricity" package should be coordinated with the "construction" department.

(d) A partial Linear Responsibility Chart for one site is given below.

Functions	Work content		
	Site selection	Cold menu	Electricity
General manager	1		
Project manager	3	1	5
Site selection manager	2		
Product and process manager	4		3
Cold dish designer		2	
Warm dish designer		3	
Construction manager	5	3	1
Electricity designer			2
Plumbing designer			3
Furniture designer			
Purchasing manager	4	4	
Advertising			
Human resources	5		

Approval levels, as determined by the project manager, are as follows:

1   must approve
2   general responsibility
3   must be consulted
4   may be consulted
5   must be notified

7.13 For the restaurant project in Exercise 7.11:

(a) In the new WBS, the second level is based on its life cycle; i.e., specification, design, execution, pilot study. The management of each work package will be assigned separately.

  1. New Restaurant Project
    1.1 Specification of needs
    1.2 Design
      1.2.1 Product design
      1.2.2 Menu design
      1.2.3 Service design
      1.2.4 Process design
      1.2.5 Purchasing design
      1.2.6 Advertisement design
      1.2.7 Labor design
        1.2.7.1 Service
        1.2.7.2 Kitchen
        1.2.7.3 Cleaning
      1.2.2 Site design
        1.2.2.1 Construction
        1.2.2.2 Electricity
        1.2.2.3 Plumbing
        1.2.2.4 Equipment
        1.2.2.4 Furniture
    1.3 Execution
      1.3.1 Purchase equipment and furnishings
      1.3.2 Launch advertising campaign
      1.3.3 Hire and train labor
        1.3.3.1 Service
        1.3.3.2 Kitchen
        1.3.3.3 Cleaning
      1.3.1 Site execution
        1.3.1.1 Construction
        1.3.1.2 Electricity
        1.3.1.3 Plumbing
        1.3.1.4 Equipment
        1.3.1.5 Furniture
    1.4 Start up

(b) Additional packages may be generated either as a result of a further division of existing packages or by identifying additional work that needs to be done. An example of an additional division is to split "Equipment" into "electric equipment" and "other equipment." Examples of two additional work packages are "audio design" and "audio execution."

7.14 Network for restaurant project in Exercise 7.11.

(a) The first step is to generate the precedence-relationships, say

Notation	Work package name	Immediate predecessor
W1	Study needs	START
W2	Restaurant survey	START
W3	Possible food	W2
W4	Possible services	W2
W5	Menu-cold dishes	W3, W1
W6	Menu-warm dishes	W3, W1
W7	Design service style	W4, W18, W1
W8	Design dining room	W5, W6, W7, W8
W9	Design process-cold dishes	W5
W10	Design process-warm dishes	W6
W11	Design outside food	W5, W6
W12	Purchase kitchen equipment	W9, W10, W11
W13	Purchase line equipment	W8
W14	Purchase dining equipment	W8
W15	Purchase perishable food	W26
W16	Purchase imperishable food	W9, W10, W11
W17	Management-all functions	START
W18	Coordination with authority	START
W19	Advertisement within campus	W28
W20	Advertisement outside	W28
W21	Construction change	W8, W9, W10, W11
W22	Electricity	W21
W23	Plumbing	W21
W24	Equipment installation	W21, W12, W13,
W25	Furniture	W21, W22, W23
W26	Start-up preparation	W25, W24, W18
W27	Pilot run	W26, W15, W30,
W28	Start up analysis	W27
W29	Labor-service requirements	W7, W24, W25
W30	Labor-service training	W29
W31	Labor-kitchen requirements	W9, W10, W24
W32	Labor-kitchen training	W31
W33	Labor-cleaning requirements	W24, W25
W34	Labor-cleaning training	W33

The Activity Network

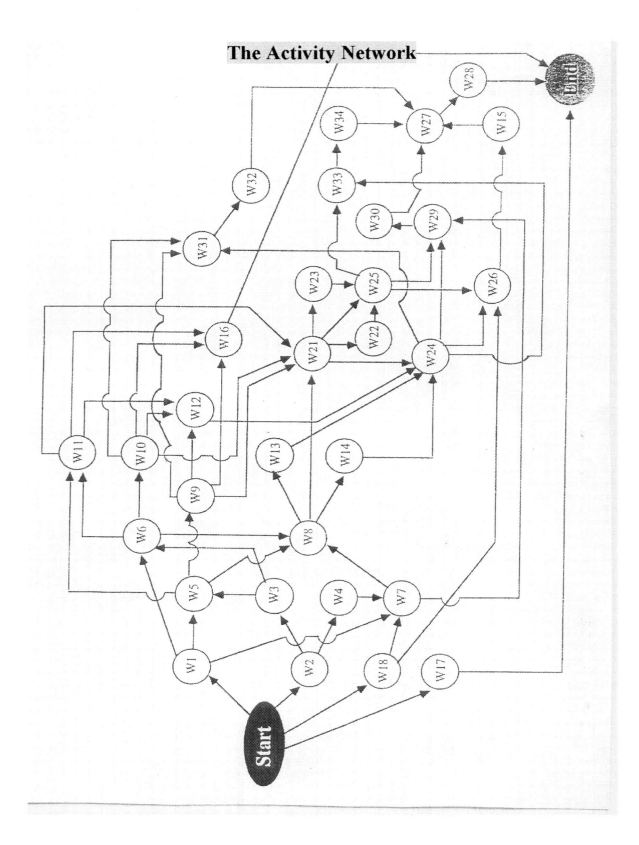

7.15 To select the best project manager for a given project the participants in the Delphi session will be asked to perform the following evaluations.

    I.   On a scale from 1 to 10 (1 = wholly inadequate, 10 = well above expectations), rank the skills and experience of each candidate.

	Candidate		
Attribute	I	II	III
Human skills			
Managerial skills			
Technical skills			
Experience			

After a few iterations of the procedure, a selection model such as the analytic hierarchy process discussed in Chapter 6, (with weights for each skill and scores for each candidate on each skill), can be used to determine the best applicant. To construct such a model, it would be necessary to first develop weights for each attribute. The simplest way to do this is for each participant to making the following assessments within the Delphi framework.

    II. On a scale from 1 to 10 (1 = insignificant, 10 = essential), rank the importance of the following skills for the job.

       1. human skills (e.g., communication, negotiation, authority)
       2. managerial skills (e.g., scheduling, budgeting, control, marketing, finance)
       3. technical skills (e.g., engineering, quality control, marketing, reliability)
       4. experience as a project manager

7.16 Legal and ethical guidelines for international projects:

    1. Consult a local authority whenever you are not sure (a lawyer concerning legal issues and a local manager concerning ethical issues).

    2. Always assume that the local law is as restrictive as the law in your own country unless informed otherwise.

    3. Never do (or undo) anything that is not considered acceptable in your own country.

7.17 – 7.18 No solutions.

CHAPTER

8. MANAGEMENT OF PRODUCT, PROCESS, AND SUPPORT DESIGN

8.1 Risk management plan for finding a job. The associated risks are:

Type	Explanation
1.	Not finding a job at all
2.	Finding jobs that are not my first choice
3.	Finding jobs at locations I do not like
4.	Having to wait for a while until a job is found

The levels of these risks are:

Risk type	Probability	Magnitude of loss	Level of risk
1	high	high	high
2	high	low	medium
3	low	high	medium
4	high	low	medium

Only risk type 1 is deemed to be high in this analysis. To be on the safe side, it is advisable to prepare a contingency plan as a hedge against not finding a job. One such plan is to apply to graduate school and work on a graduate degree until the economy has improved.

8.2 The project selected is building a new house. Important factors affecting configuration selection are:

- Family size, now and in the future
- Available budget
- Cost of land and cost of construction
- Property taxes

8.3 The configuration identification system in this case is a blueprint of the house along with a list of rooms and the design of each room.

8.4 Any changes in the design should be negotiated with the contractor. To request a change, a written request should be prepared detailing the change requested and asking the contractor for information on cost and schedule effects. The same form is then used to authorize the change. The form outline follows:

Client request
   Date_____
   New house address_____
   Owner_____
   Required change – which room or rooms are to be changed, and a short description of the changes_____

Contractor estimates
   Date_____
   Additional cost to implement change_____
   Effect of change on schedule_____
   Effect of change on warranty_____

Client decision
   Change should/should not be implemented: yes__   no__
      Client signature_____   Contractor signature_____
      Date_____   Date_____

8.5   Responsibilities for a configuration manager of a project include:

1.   To prepare a configuration identification system

2.   To design all required forms

3.   To specify computer support required for CM

4.   To train project participants in CM

5.   To develop policies and guidelines for CM

6.   To implement CM in the project

7.   To advise the change control board

8.   To check CM procedures of subcontractors and suppliers

Corresponding authority:

1.   To stop any change request not prepared properly

2.   To report on deviations from guidelines and procedures to top management

3.   To sit and participate in CCB meetings

8.6 a - Files:
1. Configuration identification file
2. File of requested changes
3. File of change requests in process
4. File of approved changes
5. Master files of configuration baseline

b - Sources of data:
1. Configuration identification – source is configuration management
2. Change request – source is any participant in the project
3. Approved changes – source is CCB
4. Configuration baselines – source is configuration management

c - Data processing requirement:
1. All transactions should go through configuration management
2. The current configuration baseline and all approved change requests can be used to redefine the original baseline
3. The status of each change request is known at all times
4. The current baseline is defined at all times

d - Required output:
1. Current baseline
2. Pending change requests and their status
3. All past baselines
4. All past CCB decisions

The flow diagram follows:

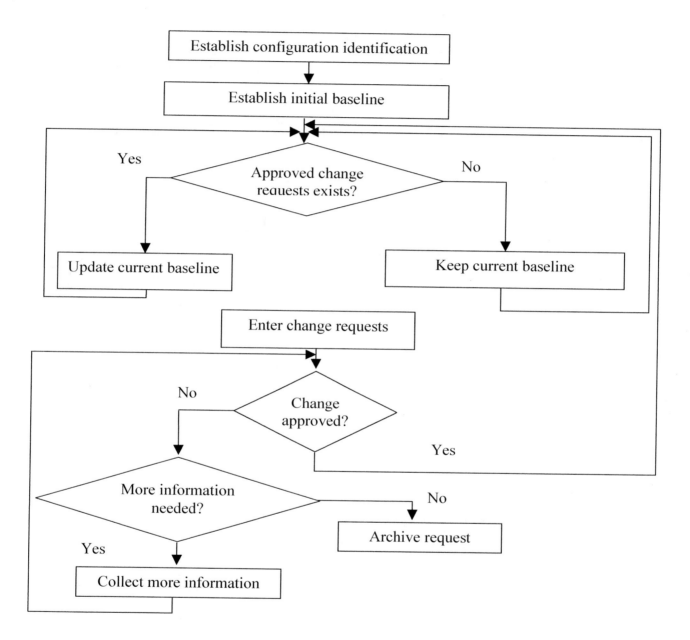

8.7 The Deming 14 points for a college:

1. Create constancy of purpose: Explain to fellow professors and students the importance of education and the need to work together for this purpose. Have class discussions to achieve commitment and understanding of the material.

2. Adopt a new philosophy: Every student must understand the course; mistakes done in homework and tests are corrected and explained to the whole class.

3. Cease dependence on mass inspection: In each class session, a small number of students will be asked to discuss the material covered in the last session. In case errors are found, the matter will be explained again.

4. End the practice of awarding business on the basis of a price tag alone; reduce the number of suppliers: Apply to the supply of lab equipment, video cassettes, etc.

5. Search for problems and improve constantly – Institute a feedback and control system for major activities: Obtain feedback from students on the quality of teaching, feedback from instructors on the quality of infrastructure and services, and so on.

6. Institute training on the job: Have teaching assistants attend the lectures.

7. Focus on leadership: Be a coach to the students, help them understand and learn.

8. Drive out fear: Have an open-door policy. Let students talk to you when they need help. Do not grade on a curve.

9. Break down barriers: Try to integrate the material in your course with that of other courses so that the students can see the whole picture.

10. Eliminate programs that ask for new levels of productivity: Give limited homework assignments and no repetitive problems.

11. Eliminate arbitrary quotas: Don't tell the students how many pages the term paper should be.

12. Remove barriers that rob people of pride in their work: Let students present their work in class; assign grades based on peer review and student comments.

13. Encourage life-long education: Be sure to keep up with your area. Read articles, do research.

14. Put everyone to work on implementing these points: Share your approach with other professors.

8.8 Crosby's 14 points:

1. Management commitment – Get the commitment of other professors and administrators to quality

2. Quality Improvement Team: Form a quality improvement team with representative professors, administrators and students

3. Quality Measurement: Develop a set of measurements for the quality of teaching, administrative support and learning

4. Cost of quality evaluation: Estimate the cost of poor teaching, poor administrative assistance and poor quality learning

5. Quality awareness: Tell professors, administrators and students about the drive for quality

6. Corrective action: As people are encouraged to talk, defective processes will come to light; take corrective actions

7. Establish an ad-hoc committee for the zero-defect program: Select three or four members of the team to develop ways to implement the zero-defect concept

8. Supervisor training: Train all levels of management so that management understands the program and each of its steps and supports it

9. Zero-defect day: Select one "DAY" as the establishment of the zero-defect program – make it a special day by announcing it in class, to faculty and to administrators

10. Goal setting: Establish goals for quality of instruction and administration assistance. Tell employees and students what the goals are

11. Error cause removal: Ask instructors, students and administrators to describe problems that cause errors; remove those causes

12. Recognition: Establish award programs – the best instructor, the best administrator, Dean's list of excellent students

13. Quality councils: Have regular meetings of team members dealing with quality to discuss the status of the program and to develop new ideas

14. Do it over again.

8.9 The plan for implementing Juran's approach in a college follows:

- The plan starts by identifying customer needs. The primary customers are students but also employers, alumni, and the local community. Focusing on the students, each will be asked to rank his or her 10 most important needs.

- Measurement will then be developed to identify the level at which the needs are satisfied by the college.

- The processes used to achieve target performance levels will also be developed. These will be accompanied by evaluation and control mechanisms.

- Implementation of all processes will be monitored at the course level, the department level, and college level to guarantee quality objectives are being met.

8.10 The plan for implementing Juran's approach in an academic department follows:

- The program starts by identifying the needs of the customers – the students. Each student will be asked to rank his or her 10 most important needs.

- Next, a method of measurement will be developed to identify the level at which the needs are satisfied by the academic department.

- The processes used to achieve target performance levels will also be developed. These will be accompanied by evaluation and control mechanisms.

- Implementation of these processes will be monitored at the course level and department level to ensure quality goals are being met.

8.11 The reward system will be based on performance. For the IPT members the objectives are time to market, cost, and quality of the product and the degree to which customer satisfaction is achieved. Thus, a group reward system or multifactor reward system is needed in which all members of the IPT share the same reward. This will encourage cooperation and teamwork.

8.12 (a) In a matrix organization, the dual boss system dictates that performance evaluations be conducted by both the functional manager and the project manager to ensure a proper balance between the project-related activities and the functional activities of the team members.

(b) In a project organization, members of the IPT belong to the project only so the mission, the goal, and the evaluation criteria are project based. Thus, the performance evaluation is the responsibility of the project manager or his superiors.

8.13 The QFD matrix follows.

Whats / hows	Lectures	Book	Software	Case studies	Homework
Theory	+	+	*	*	+
Practice	+	*	+	+	+
"Hands on" experience	*	*	+	+	+

+ Strong positive correlation
* Weak positive correlation

8.14 The major risks of the U.S. military operation to oust Saadam Hussein from power in Iraq in 2003 are listed below.

Event	Probability	Damage	Risk
Shortages of personnel	low	high	med
Shortages of equipment	low	high	med
Shortages of supplies	low	high	med
Iraq uses chemical weapons	high	high	high
Iraq uses nuclear weapons	low	high	low

At the beginning of the operation, enough personnel, equipment and supplies were available so the probability of any shortages occurring in these areas was low. The probability that Iraq had nuclear weapons was also low based on intelligence. The only high risk was that Iraq might use chemical weapons. To manage this risk, the troops were equipped with chemical warfare gear; however, most of Iraq's air force was destroyed immediately so their ability to deliver chemical bombs from the air was eliminated. Also, suspected caches of chemical weapons were destroyed in the early days of the war

8.15 A concurrent engineering (CE) approach supports time-based competition by replacing sequential engineering with concurrent or parallel design of new products. In particular, the design of production operations and maintenance infrastructure is performed concurrently with product design. A prime objective of CE is to shorten the time from conception to market. Shorter project duration means lower overhead and hence, decreasing overhead costs.

8.16 Configuration management (CM) concentrates on the management of technology by identifying and controlling the physical and functional characteristics of a product or a system, and its supporting documentation. The medium of implementation is a set of tools designed to provide accurate information on what is to be built, what is currently being built, and what has been built in the past. Configuration management is needed when CE is used because engineers who deal with different aspects of the design, work simultaneously (product, process, operations and maintenance design). It is essential to keep all team members updated as change requests are made and approved. Without a proper CM system, it is difficult to guarantee that everybody involved in the design effort is working on the same configuration; i.e., the configuration based on the most recent baseline and all approved changes. Furthermore, it is difficult to keep all team members informed of all pending changes or to solicit their advice on the effect that proposed changes will have on the project.

8.17 Concurrent engineering reduces time to market and ensures proper coordination between the different design aspects of the project, such as product design, process design and support design. By reducing the project duration, overhead cost is reduced as well. The major problem with concurrent engineering is the difficulty associated with coordinating the design effort and the risk of integration problems as a result of poor communication among the members of the design team during the design process. A well-managed design process and proper application of configuration management can reduce the risks associated with concurrent engineering while keeping the benefits.

The pros of concurrent engineering are:

1. Replaces the conventional engineering approach in which new product development is initialed by a single organizational unit

2. Shortens the time from conception to market

3. Reduces the length of the design process; overhead and management costs are reduced proportionally

4. Leads to a higher market share and consequently, higher sales and profits

The cons of concurrent engineering are:

1. Using CE is risky, and without proper technological and risk management plans in place, the results can be calamitous.

2. CE is only beneficial in projects that have the following characteristics:
    *   The project has engineering and/or R&D work content in it (i.e., the design of a new system or the development of a new technology)
    *   The team has experience with the underlying technology
    *   The team has received training in quality management and has had the opportunity to apply the concepts in its work
    *   The goal is a product or family of products with clearly defined features and functions
    *   Success is not dependent on invention or significant innovation

CHAPTER

9. PROJECT SCHEDULING

9.1   (a) AOA network

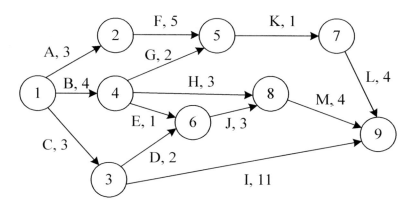

(b) AON network

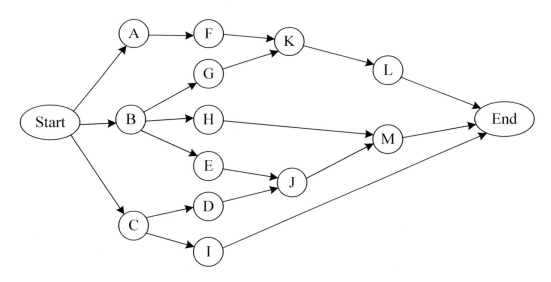

(c) Critical path analysis for AOA network

Event, i	Early time, t_i	Late time, T_i	Total slack	Critical
1	0	0	0	yes
2	3	4	1	
3	3	3	0	yes
4	4	6	2	
5	8	9	1	
6	5	7	2	
7	9	10	1	
8	8	10	2	
9	14	14	0	yes

Critical path: events $1 \rightarrow 3 \rightarrow 9$ and activities C and I.

(d) Total slack and free slack.

Activity	(i, j)	L_{ij}	$ES_{ij} = t_i$	$LF_{ij} = T_j$	Total slack, TS_{ij}	Free slack, FS_{ij}
A	(1, 2)	3	0	4	1	0
B	(1, 4)	4	0	6	2	0
C	(1, 3)	3	0	3	0	0
D	(3, 6)	2	3	7	2	0
E	(4, 6)	1	4	7	2	0
F	(2, 5)	5	3	9	1	0
G	(4, 5)	2	4	9	3	2
H	(4, 8)	3	4	10	3	1
I	(3, 9)	11	3	14	0	0
J	(6, 8)	3	5	10	2	0
K	(5, 7)	1	8	10	1	0
L	(7, 9)	4	9	14	1	1
M	(8, 9)	4	8	14	2	2

(e) Assume beta distribution and compute expected time and variance for uncertain activities.

Activity	Expected time	Variance
A	$23/6 = 3.83$	$(3/6)^2 = 0.25$
C	$17/6 = 2.83$	$(3/6)^2 = 0.25$
I	$67/6 = 11.16$	$(7/5)^2 = 1.36$

Mistake should be 6 [handwritten annotation]

For C-I the critical path, we get:

Expected duration $= 2.83 + 11.16 = 14$

Standard deviation $= (0.25 + 1.36)^{1/2} = 1.27$

The required probabilities are:

D (days)	$z = (D - 14)/1.27$	Prob. to complete
10	−3.14	0.0008
12	−1.57	0.0582
14	0	0.5
16	1.57	0.9418
18	3.14	0.9992
20	4.72	1

9.2 Estimate the time it will take you to learn a new computer software package that combines a spreadsheet with statistical analysis. Explain how the estimate was made and what accuracy you think it has.

In this case a modular technique approach can be applied. The software learning process can be decomposed in the following activities:

- General understanding of the program menu structure	10 hours
- Spreadsheet format and functions	25 hours
- Statistical analysis theory	75 hours
- Statistical analysis built in functions	10 hours
- Spreadsheet input data format for statistical analysis	10 hours
- Statistical analysis process	20 hours
- Statistic output data interpretation	5 hours
- Output report generation	5 hours
Total:	160 hours

If it is assumed that we have no previous experience with this kind of activity and that no information is available on the real characteristics of the software package such as format, number of built-in functions, and complexity of data management, the accuracy of the above estimate would be low. To better estimate the learning time, we would need to have a higher level of knowledge and understanding of the problem. If prior experience existed, it might be appropriate to use a learning curve.

9.3   One set of modules time estimates are as follows.

Module	Estimated time (hours)
Definition of objectives	10
Definition of required data	20
Data collection	50
Data analysis	40
Writing of proposal	50
Review and corrections	10
Total	180

9.4   Use the benchmark job technique to estimate the time required to type a 50-page paper and prepare figures using a computer graphic package.

Text capture:	8 min/page
Format:	5 min general + 1 min/page
Spelling check:	2 min/page
Tables:	3 min general + 0.1 min/cell
Figure development:	15 min./figure
Figure insertion and format:	3 min/page
Printing:	0.5 min/page

Considering the job of typing a 50-page paper, with 28 figures and 23 tables of approximately 20 cells each, we can calculate the required time as follows:

$$t = 50(8) + [5 + 1(50)] + 50(2) + 23[3 + 0.1(20)] + 28(15) + 28(3) + 50(0.5)$$
$$= 1199 \text{ min} = 20 \text{ hours}$$

9.5   The following variables and data are used for the regression analysis.

Paper no.	Length (pages), X_1	Number of tables, X_2	Time required (hours), Y
1	5	3	1
2	10	5	2
3	19	9	4
4	12	3	2
5	21	6	4
6	30	10	6
7	24	6	3
8	17	4	2
9	19	8	4
10	32	8	5

Regression equation: Time $= b_0 + b_1$(Number of pages) $+ b_2$(number of tables)

$$Y = b_0 + b_1X_1 + b_2X_2$$

$$Y = -0.53 + 0.08X_1 + 0.36X_2$$

$R^2 = 0.94$, Adjusted $R^2 = 0.92$, standard error of estimate $= 0.4427$

Descriptive statistics for regression analysis ($n = 10$)

	X_1	X_2	Y
Average	17.4000	6.2000	3.3000
Std Dev	4.8120	2.4855	1.5670
Correlation matrix			
X_1	1	0.6429	0.7633
X_2	0.6429	1	0.9243
Y	0.7633	0.9243	1

Analysis of variance

Source	SS	df	MS	F-value	Level of significance
Regression	20.728	2	10.364	52.88	0.00006
Residual	1.372	7	0.196		
Total	21.100	9			

9.6 Designing a new house.

Activity	Duration (days)	Predecessor
A. Meet with client	1	—
B. Visit location of the new house	1	A
C. Prepare a rough draft of layout	2	B
D. Get client approval and revisions	5	C
E. Detailed design of construction	3	D
F. Detailed design electrical/communication lines	2	D
G. Detailed design of plumbing	4	D
H. Design of landscape	1	D
I. Client final approval and revisions	5	EFGH
J. Preparation of final drawings and documents	2	I

The only uncertainty is likely to be in activities A, D and I where the client is involved and revisions may be needed. For an experienced builder's point of view, most other activities are routine in projects of this type so their duration can be estimated quite accurately.

9.7

Activity	ES	EF	LS	LF	Slack	Critical
A	0	1	0	1	0	yes
B	1	2	1	2	0	yes
C	2	4	2	4	0	yes
D	4	9	4	9	0	yes
E	9	12	10	13	1	no
F	9	11	11	13	2	no
G	9	13	9	13	0	yes
H	9	10	12	13	3	yes
I	13	18	13	18	0	yes
J	18	20	18	20	0	yes

Gantt Chart

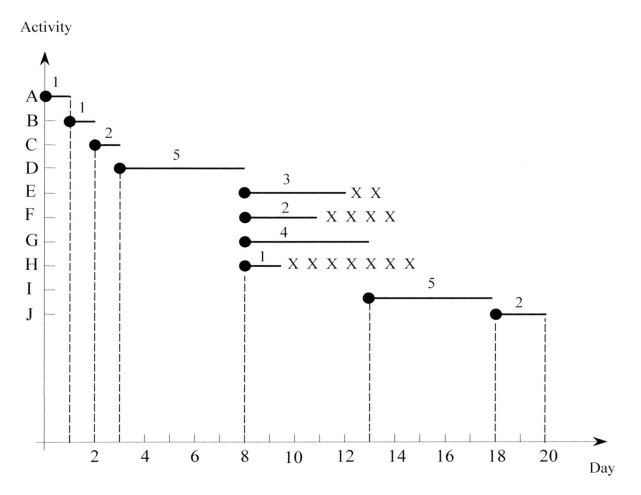

x x x x Slack of noncritical activities. All activities with no slack are critical.

9.8 The AOA network:

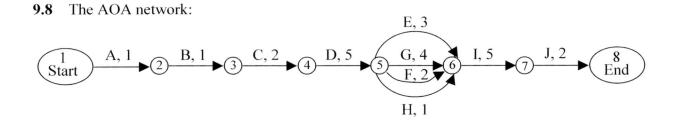

The activity time and slack values are calculated in Exercise 7-7.

Event	Early time	Late time
1	0	0
2	1	1
3	2	2
4	4	4
5	9	9
6	13	13
7	18	18
8	20	20

9.9 The AOA network

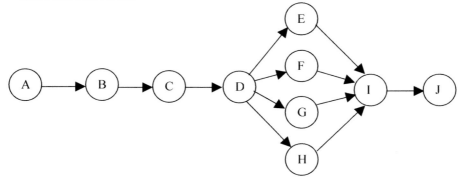

9.10 The linear programming model is based on the AOA network in Exercise 9.8. The following notation is used.

t_i = time of event i

L_j = duration of activity j

Model

Minimize t_8

subject to $t_8 - t_7 \geq L_J$ or $t_8 - t_7 \geq 2$

$t_7 - t_6 \geq L_I$ or $t_7 - t_6 \geq 5$

$t_6 - t_5 \geq L_H$ or $t_6 - t_5 \geq 1$

$t_6 - t_5 \geq L_G$ or $t_6 - t_5 \geq 4$

$t_6 - t_5 \geq L_F$ or $t_6 - t_5 \geq 2$

$t_6 - t_5 \geq L_E$ or $t_6 - t_5 \geq 3$

$t_5 - t_4 \geq L_D$ or $t_5 - t_4 \geq 5$

$t_4 - t_3 \geq L_C$ or $t_4 - t_3 \geq 2$

$$t_3 - t_2 \geq L_B \ \text{ or } \ t_3 - t_2 \geq 1$$

$$t_2 - t_1 \geq L_A \ \text{ or } \ t_2 - t_1 \geq 1$$

$$t_i \geq 0, \, i = 1, \ldots, 8$$

9.10   Designing and building a new house.

Activity	Immediate predecessors	Duration (days)
A. Select a location	--	30
B. Design house	A	20
C. Get a building permit	B	30
D. Select a contractor	B	20
E. Order materials	C, D	10
F. Material delivery	E	20
G. Excavation	D	30
H. Landscaping	D	40
I. Foundation	G	10
J. Erection of walls	F, I	20
K. Roof	J	10
L. Electrical work	K	10
M. Doors and windows	J	10
N. Plumbing	J	10
O. Painting	K, L, M, N	10
P. Finishing	H, O	10

AOA network

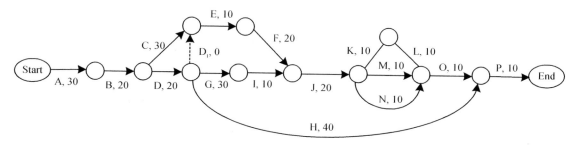

9.12   The critical paths in this project are:

$$A - B - C - E - F - J - K - L - O - P$$

$$A - B - D - G - I - J - K - L - O - P$$

The duration of each is 170 days. Assuming that there are 30 days in each month, the critical path has to be shortened by 60 days. Every other path longer than 170 – 60 – 110 has to be shortened to 110 days as well. From the AOA network, we see that the two critical paths have a string of three activities that differ: C – E – F in the first case and D – G – I in the second. One approach then would be to try to reduce the times of the other activities on the critical path by 60 days. In addition, it might be possible to perform A and B in parallel. Of course, care must be taken when reducing critical activities when there non-critical activities that are performed in parallel. At some point, a critical activity may become non-critical and vice versa.

9.13

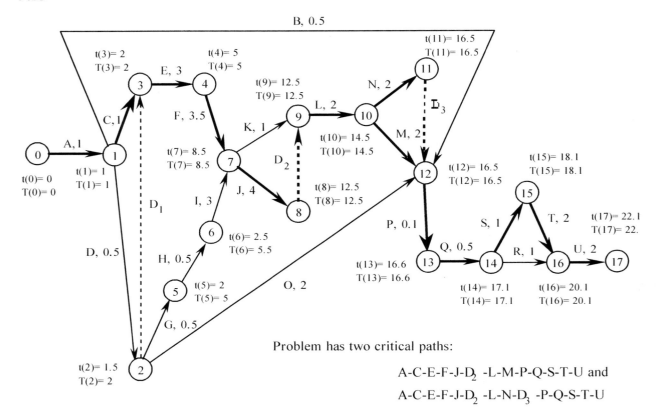

Problem has two critical paths:

A-C-E-F-J-D_2 -L-M-P-Q-S-T-U and

A-C-E-F-J-D_2 -L-N-D_3 -P-Q-S-T-U

9.14

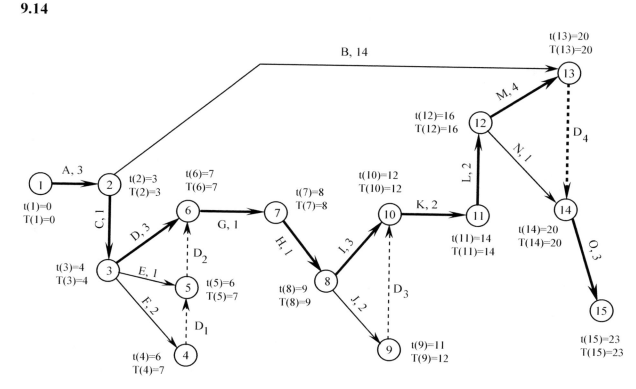

Critical path: A-C-D-G-H-I-K-L-M-D$_4$-O

9.15

Activity	(i,j)	L_{ij}	$ES_{ij} = t_i$	$EF_{ij} = ES_{ij} + L_{ij}$	$LF_{ij} = T_j$	$LS_{ij} = LF_{ij} - L_{ij}$	$TS_{ij} = LS_{ij} - ES_{ij}$	$FS_{ij} = t_j - t_i - L_{ij}$
A	(0,1)	3	0	3	3	0	0	0
B	(1,3)	14	3	17	20	16	13	0
C	(1,2)	1	3	4	4	3	0	0
D	(2,6)	3	4	7	7	4	0	0
E	(2,5)	1	4	5	7	6	2	0
F	(2,4)	2	4	6	7	5	1	0
G	(6,7)	1	7	8	8	7	0	0
H	(7,8)	1	8	9	9	8	0	0
I	(8,10)	3	9	12	12	9	0	0
J	(8,9)	2	9	11	12	10	1	0
K	(10,11)	2	12	14	14	12	0	0
L	(11,12)	2	14	16	16	14	0	0
M	(12,13)	4	16	20	20	16	0	0
N	(12,14)	1	16	17	20	19	3	3
O	(14,15)	3	20	23	23	20	0	0

9.16

Project (a):

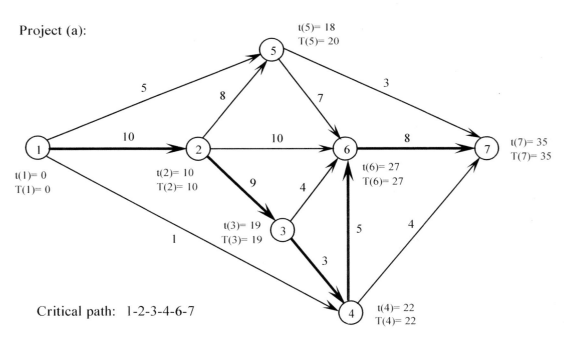

Critical path: 1-2-3-4-6-7

Project (b):

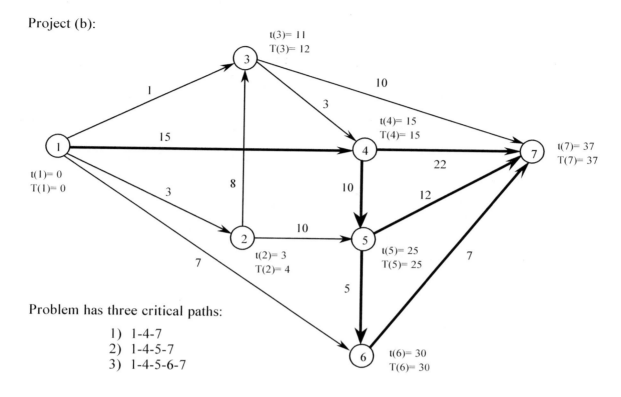

Problem has three critical paths:

    1) 1-4-7
    2) 1-4-5-7
    3) 1-4-5-6-7

9.17   *Project (a):*

Activity	Duration	Earliest		Latest		Total slack	Free slack
		Start	Finish	Start	Finish		
(i,j)	L_{ij}	ES_{ij}	EF_{ij}	LS_{ij}	LF_{ij}	TS_{ij}	FS_{ij}
(1,2)	10	0	10	0	10	0*	0
(1,4)	1	0	1	21	22	21	21
(1,5)	5	0	5	15	20	15	13
(2,3)	9	10	19	10	19	0*	0
(2,5)	8	10	18	12	20	2	0
(2,6)	10	10	20	17	27	7	7
(3,4)	3	19	22	19	22	0*	0
(3,6)	4	19	23	23	27	4	4
(4,6)	5	22	27	22	27	0*	0
(4,7)	4	22	26	31	35	9	9
(5,6)	7	18	25	20	27	2	2
(5,7)	3	18	21	32	35	14	14
(6,7)	8	27	35	27	35	0*	0

*on critical path

Project (b):

Activity (i,j)	Duration L_{ij}	Earliest Start ES_{ij}	Finish EF_{ij}	Latest Start LS_{ij}	Finish LF_{ij}	Total slack TS_{ij}	Free slack FS_{ij}
(1,2)	3	0	3	1	4	1	0
(1,3)	1	0	1	11	12	11	10
(1,4)	15	0	15	0	15	0*	0
(1,6)	7	0	7	23	30	23	23
(2,3)	8	3	11	4	12	1	0
(2,5)	10	3	13	15	25	12	12
(3,4)	3	11	14	12	15	1	1
(3,7)	10	11	21	27	37	16	16
(4,5)	10	15	25	15	25	0*	0
(4,7)	22	15	37	15	37	0*	0
(5,6)	5	25	30	25	30	0*	0
(5,7)	12	25	37	25	37	0*	0
(6,7)	7	30	37	30	37	0*	0

*on critical path

9.18 *Project (a):*

Activity	$\bar{\varphi}_{ij}$	v_{ij}	Activity	$\bar{\varphi}_{ij}$	v_{ij}
(1,2)	6.17	0.25	(3,6)	4.00	0.109
(1,4)	2.83	0.25	(4,6)	7.67	1.00
(1,5)	3.83	0.25	(4,7)	6.17	0.25
(2,3)	5.00	0.109	(5,6)	10.67	1.00
(2,5)	8.17	0.25	(5,7)	6.00	0.444
(2,6)	9.50	0.689	(6,7)	4.00	0.109
(3,4)	8.50	0.689			

Probabilities:

Event	Path	$E(X)$	$V(X)$	τ†	$P(X \le \tau)$
1	–	–	–	–	–
2	(1,2)	6.17	0.250	6.17	0.50
3	(1,2,3)	11.17	0.359	11.17	0.50
4	(1,2,3,4)	19.67	1.048	19.67	0.50
5	(1,2,5)‡	14.34	0.500	16.67	1.00
6	(1,2,3,4,6)*	27.34	2.048	27.34	0.50
7	(1,2,3,4,6,7)	31.34	2.157	31.34	0.50

† obtained by carrying out critical path calculations using $\ddot{a}_{ij}$

‡ longest of {(1,25), (1,5)}

* longest of {(1,5,6), (1,2,5,6), (1,2,6), (1,2,3,6), (1,2,3,4,6), (1,4,6)}

Project (b):

Activity	$\ddot{a}_{ij}$	v_{ij}	Activity	$\ddot{a}_{ij}$	v_{ij}
(1,2)	2.83	0.250	(3,7)	13.00	0.109
(1,3)	6.83	0.250	(4,5)	12.17	0.689
(1,4)	7.17	0.250	(4,7)	10.00	0.444
(1,6)	2.00	0.109	(5,6)	8.33	0.444
(2,3)	4.00	0.109	(5,7)	4.33	1.000
(2,5)	8.00	0.109	(6,7)	6.00	0.109
(3,4)	15.00	2.800			

Probabilities:

Event	Path	$E(X)$	$V(X)$	τ	$P(X \le \tau)$
1	–	–	–	–	–
2	(1,2)	2.83	0.250	2.83	0.50
3	(1,2,3) [larger var. than (1,3)]	6.83	0.359	6.83	0.50
4	(1,2,3,4)	21.83	3.159	21.83	0.50
5	(1,2,3,4,5)	34.00	3.848	34.00	0.50
6	(1,2,3,4,5,6)	42.33	4.292	42.33	0.50
7	(1,2,3,4,5,6,7)	48.33	4.401	48.33	0.50

9.19   (a)

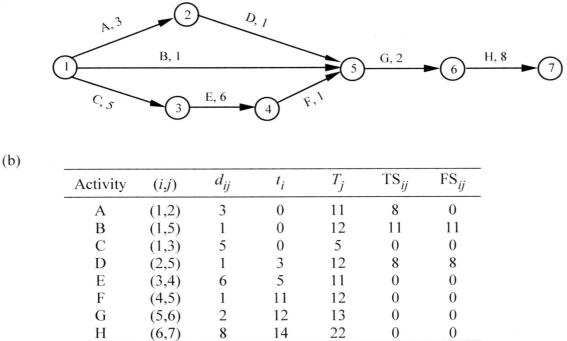

(b)

Activity	(i,j)	d_{ij}	t_i	T_j	TS_{ij}	FS_{ij}
A	(1,2)	3	0	11	8	0
B	(1,5)	1	0	12	11	11
C	(1,3)	5	0	5	0	0
D	(2,5)	1	3	12	8	8
E	(3,4)	6	5	11	0	0
F	(4,5)	1	11	12	0	0
G	(5,6)	2	12	13	0	0
H	(6,7)	8	14	22	0	0

For activity A or (1,2), for example, $TS_{12} = 8$ means that A can be delayed up to 8 weeks without delaying the 22 week earliest completion time for the project; however, $FS_{12} = 0$ shows that this slack is completely shared with activity D so any delay in the start of A reduces the slack available to D by the amount of the delay.

(c) The critical path is: C-E-F-G-H or 1-3-4-5-6-7; a delay in any one of these activities delays the entire project beyond 22 weeks.

(d)

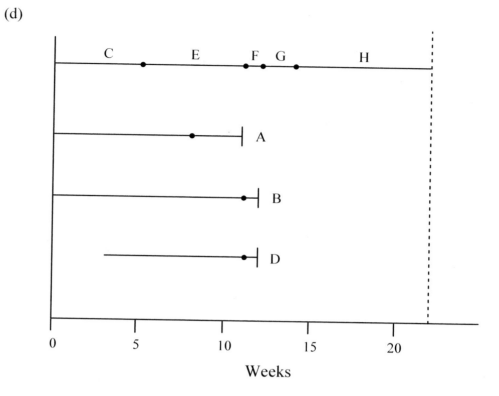

Weeks

9.20 (a) & (b)

Activity	(i,j)	$\bar{t}_{ij}$	v_{ij}	t_i	T_j	TS_{ij}	FS_{ij}
A	(1,2)	2.8	0.25	0	12.4	9.6	0
B	(1,5)	1.2	0.03	0	13.4	12.2	12.2
C	(1,3)	5.5	0.69	0	5.5	0	0
D	(2,5)	1.0	0	2.8	13.4	9.6	9.6
E	(3,4)	6.7	1.78	5.5	12.2	0	0
F	(4,5)	1.2	0.03	12.2	13.4	0	0
G	(5,6)	2.0	0.11	13.4	15.4	0	0
H	(6,7)	8.0	0.44	15.4	23.4	0	0

Total slack and free slack increase compared to Exercise 9.19. Expected durations also generally increase.

(c) No.

(d) Let X_7 denote the critical path. $E(X_7) = 23.4$, $V(X_7) = 3.05$

    (1) $P(X_7 \le 22) = P(Z_7 \le -0.80) = 0.21$

    (2) $P(X_7 \le 23.4) = 0.5$

    (3) $P(X_7 > 30) = 1 - P(X_7 \le 30) = 1 - P(Z_7 \le 3.78) = 1 - 1.0 = 0$

9.21   (a) & (b)

Activity	(i,j)	$\ddot{a}_{ij}$	v_{ij}	t_i	T_j	TS_{ij}	FS_{ij}
A	(1,2)	2.7	0.85	0	13.7	11.0	0
B	(1,5)	1.3	0.09	0	14.7	13.4	13.4
C	(1,3)	6.0	2.37	0	6.0	0	0
D	(2,5)	1.0	0	2.7	14.7	11.0	11.0
E	(3,4)	7.4	6.06	6.0	13.4	0	0
F	(4,5)	1.3	0.09	13.4	14.7	0	0
G	(5,6)	2.0	0.38	14.7	16.7	0	0
H	(6,7)	8.0	1.51	16.7	24.7	0	0

Differences: When the distribution is positively skewed ($\ddot{a}_{ij} > m_{ij}$), Eq. (9.14) yields higher values for $\ddot{a}_{ij}$ than does Eq. (9.2). See activities B, C, E, F. The reverse is true for negatively skewed distributions. See activity A. When the distributions are symmetric, both formulas give the identical results ($\ddot{a}_{ij} = m_{ij}$). Except for the case where all time estimates are the same (e.g., activity D), the standard deviation (variance) given by Eq. (9.15) is always greater than the standard deviation given by Eq. (9.1).

(c) No.

(d) Let X_7 denote the critical path; $E(X_7) = 24.7$, $V(X_7) = 10.41$

    (1) $P(X_7 \le 22) = P(Z_7 \le -0.84) = 0.20$

    (2) $P(X_7 \le 24.7) = 0.5$

    (3) $P(X_7 > 30) = 1 - P(X_7 \le 30) = 1 - P(Z_7 \le 1.64) = 1 - 0.95 = 0.05$

9.22 (a)

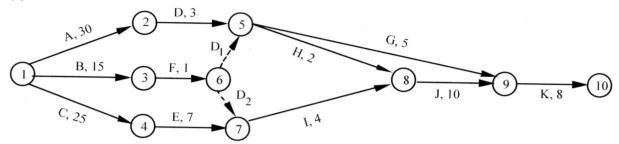

(b)

Activity	(i,j)	d_{ij}	t_i	T_j	TS_{ij}	FS_{ij}
A	(1,2)	30	0	31	1	0
B	(1,3)	15	0	31	16	0
C	(1,4)	25	0	25	0	0
D	(2,5)	3	30	34	1	0
E	(4,7)	7	25	32	0	0
F	(3,6)	1	15	32	16	0
D_1	(6,7)	0	16	32	16	16
D_2	(6,5)	0	16	34	18	17
G	(5,9)	5	33	46	8	8
H	(5,8)	2	33	36	1	1
I	(7,8)	4	32	36	0	0
J	(8,9)	10	36	46	0	0
K	(9,10)	8	46	54	0	0

For activity B or (1,3), for example, $TS_{13} = 16$ means that we can delay B up to 16 days without delaying the 54-day earliest completion time for the project; however, $FS_{13} = 0$ shows that this slack is completely shared with activities in series with B; i.e., any delay in B reduces available slack to succeeding activities.

(c) C-E-I-J-K or 1-4-7-8-9.10; a delay in any one of these activities delays the entire project beyond 54 days.

(d)

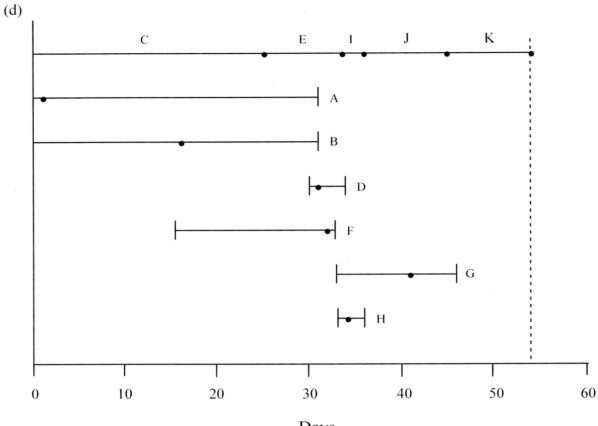

The scheduling of A, D and H is tight, as only one day of slack exists between earliest and latest starting dates. Considerably more slack exists for B and F (16 days), while G is fairly flexible (8 days).

9.23   (a) & (b)

Activity	(i,j)	$\hat{\varphi}_{ij}$	v_{ij}	t_i	T_j	TS_{ij}	FS_{ij}
A	(1,2)	31.7	11.1	0	32.1	0.4	0
B	(1,3)	15.0	2.8	0	32.3	17.3	0
C	(1,4)	25.8	6.2	0	25.8	0	0
D	(2,5)	3.3	0.1	31.7	35.4	0.4	0
E	(4,7)	7.5	1.4	25.8	33.3	0	0
F	(3,6)	1.0	0	15.0	33.3	17.3	0
D_1	(6,7)	0	0	16.0	33.3	17.3	17.3
D_2	(6,5)	0	0	16.0	35.4	19.4	19.0
G	(5,9)	5.2	0.2	35.0	47.9	7.7	7.7
H	(5,8)	2.2	0	35.0	37.6	0.4	0.4
I	(7,8)	4.3	0.1	33.3	37.6	0	0
J	(8,9)	10.3	1.0	37.6	47.9	0	0
K	(9,10)	8.8	2.2	47.9	56.7	0	0

Total slack and free slack increase compared to Exercise 9.22. Expected durations also generally increase.

(c)   No.

(d)   Let X_{10} denote the critical path; $E(X_{10}) = 56.7$, $V(X_{10}) = 10.9$

(1) $P(X_{10} \leq 54) = P(Z_{10} \leq -0.82) = 0.21$

(2) $P(X_{10} \leq 56.7) = 0.5$

(3) $P(X_{10} > 70) = 1 - P(X_{10} \leq 70) = 1 - P(Z_{10} \leq 4.0) = 1 - 1 = 0$

9.24   (a) & (b)

Activity	(i,j)	$\ddot{a}_{ij}$	v_{ij}	t_i	T_j	TS_{ij}	FS_{ij}
A	(1,2)	33.4	37.9	0	33.4	0	0
B	(1,3)	15.0	9.5	0	33.7	18.7	0
C	(1,4)	26.7	21.3	0	26.7	0	0
D	(2,5)	3.7	0.4	33.4	37.1	0	0
E	(4,7)	8.0	4.6	26.7	34.7	0	0
F	(3,6)	1.0	0	15.0	34.7	18.7	0
D_1	(6,7)	0	0	16.0	34.7	18.7	18.7
D_2	(6,5)	0	0	16.0	37.1	21.1	21.1
G	(5,9)	5.3	0.9	37.1	50.1	7.7	7.7
H	(5.8)	2.3	0.1	37.1	39.4	0	0
I	(7,8)	4.7	0.4	34.7	39.4	0	0
J	(8,9)	10.7	3.4	39.4	50.1	0	0
K	(9,10)	9.7	7.7	50.1	59.8	0	0

See comments in Exercise 9.21.

(c) Yes and no. To the first decimal place, two paths are now critical: A-D-H-J-K and C-E-I-J-K; denote the critical path by X_{10}.

(d) $E(X_{10}) = 59.8$, $V(X_{10}) = \max\{49.5, 37.4\} = 49.5$

   (1) $P(X_{10} \le 54) = P(Z_{10} \le -0.82) = 0.21$
   (2) $P(X_{10} \le 59.8) = 0.5$
   (3) $P(X_{10} > 70) = 1 - P(Z_{10} \le 1.45) = 1 - 0.93 = 0.07$

9.25   (a) The data for the problem are repeated below.

Activity	Frequency	Percentage
Machine is working on a job	67	64.4
Parts are fed to the machine	6	5.8
Maintenance is performed	9	8.7
Machine is waiting for parts	22	21.1
	104	100.0

During the 64.4% of the time the machine was working on a job, it was being fed parts or maintenance was being performed 5.8% + 8.7% = 14.5% of the time. Therefore, the actual utilization was

$$\frac{64.4}{64.4 + 14.5} = 0.82$$

Because the design capacity is 0.4, the actual capacity is $0.4 \times 0.82 = 0.328$ boards per hour.

(b) Time $= 60/0.328 = 183$ hours

(c) For a normal distribution, a 95% level of confidence corresponds to $z = 1.96$. Let
N = sample size
P = fraction to be estimated
z = value of standard normal deviate corresponding to desired confidence interval
α = desired accuracy

The following formula can be used to determine the sample size

$$N = \frac{1-P}{P}\left(\frac{z}{\alpha}\right)^2$$

$$= \frac{1-0.644}{0.644}\left(\frac{1.96}{0.05}\right)^2 \cong 850$$

9.26 (a) The parametric equation should calculate the machine capacity as a function of the circuit board configuration. The equation might be based on past performance and determined with a technique like regression analysis. The following data elements might be used in the analysis.

T = time per board (dependent variable

X_1 = board size, cm^2 (independent variable)

X_2 = batch size (independent variable)

X_3 = number of components (independent variable)

X_4 = number of details (independent variable)

X_5 = number of transistors (independent variable)

(b) Here is one parameter equation obtained with multiple regression analysis

$$T = 254 + 0.07X1 + 3.03X_2 + 2.04X_3 + 0.79X_4 + 0.015X_5$$

If a circuit board as the following configuration, for example,

$$X_1 = 1000,\ X_2 = 100,\ X_3 = 120,\ X_4 = 90,\ X_5 = 18,000$$

then substituting these values in the above equations gives $T = 1212.9$ hours.

(c) The analysis assumes that (1) there are no changes in the work methods, (2) the machine is used correctly and the operators work efficiently, and (3) the parametric equation is able to properly represent the relationship. This can be verified by examining the correlation coefficient for the regression analysis.

9.27 (a) Early start Gantt chart

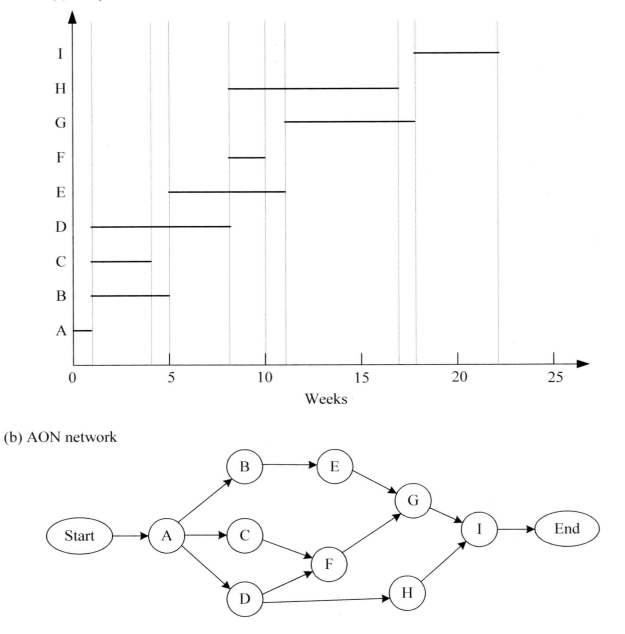

(b) AON network

(c) AOA network

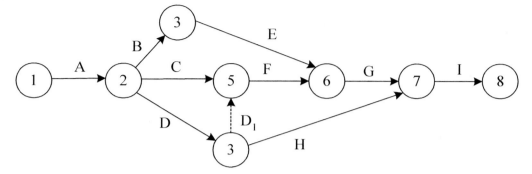

(d) Possible paths and durations.

Path	Duration (weeks)
A-B-E-G-I	22
A-C-F-G-I	17
A-D-D_1-F-G-I	21
A-D-H-I	21

The critical path is A-B-E-G-I. It will take 22 weeks to complete the project.

(e) and (f) Calculation of for activity start and finish times and slacks.

Activity	(i, j)	L_{ij}	ES_{ij}	EF_{ij}	LF_{ij}	LS_{ij}	TS_{ij}	FS_{ij}
A	(1, 2)	1	0	1	1	0	0	0
B	(2, 3)	4	1	5	5	1	0	0
C	(2, 5)	3	1	4	9	6	5	4
D	(2, 4)	7	1	8	9	2	1	0
E	(3, 6)	6	5	11	11	5	0	0
F	(5, 6)	2	8	10	11	9	1	1
G	(6, 7)	7	11	18	18	11	0	0
H	(7, 8)	9	8	17	18	9	1	1
I	(4, 7)	4	18	22	22	18	0	0

9.28 (a) First let us calculate the expected value $\ddot{\wp}$ and standard deviation $\ddot{o}$ of activities D and E, where

$$\ddot{\wp} = \frac{a + 4 \cdot b + c}{6} \qquad\qquad \ddot{o} = \frac{c - a}{6}$$

$$\ddot{\wp}(D) = \frac{6 + 4 \cdot 7 + 8}{6} = 7 \qquad\qquad \ddot{o}(D) = \frac{8 - 6}{6} = 0.33$$

$$\ddot{\wp}(E) = \frac{5 + 4 \cdot 6 + 9}{6} = 6.33 \qquad\qquad \ddot{o}(E) = \frac{9 - 5}{6} = 0.67$$

For the project to be completed within 22 weeks, all paths must be completed in 22 weeks or less. We will examine each path one at a time. In the analysis, we let X_i be the completion time of path $i = 1, \ldots, 4$ and make use of Eq. (9.12).

Path A-B-E-G-I: Because E is the only uncertain activity, we are interested in $P(\text{E} \le 6$ weeks). Letting

$$z = \frac{6 - \ddot{\wp}(E)}{\ddot{o}(E)} = \frac{6 - 6.33}{0.67} = -0.5$$

we have $P(\text{E} \le 6) = P(Z \le -0.5) = 1 - P(Z \le 0.5) = 1 - 0.69 = 0.31$ from Table 9C.1. Therefore,

$$P(\text{A-B-E-G-I} \le 22 \text{ weeks}) = P(X_1 \le 22) = 0.31$$

Note that this analysis is based on the assumption that the time to compute activity E is normally distributed.

The probability of completing the activities on the other paths within 22 weeks is computed in the same manner.

Path A-C-F-G-I: There are no uncertain activities so

$$P(\text{A-C-F-G-I} \le 22 \text{ weeks}) = P(X_2 \le 22) = 1$$

Path A-D-D$_1$-F-G-I: Because D is the only uncertain activity, we are interested in $P(\text{D} \le 8$ weeks). Letting

$$z = \frac{8 - \ddot{\wp}(D)}{\ddot{o}(D)} = \frac{8 - 7}{0.33} = 3$$

we have $P_3(\text{D} \le 8) = P(Z \le 3) = 0.9987$ from Table 9C.1. Therefore,

$$P(\text{A-D-D}_1\text{-F-G-I} \le 22 \text{ weeks}) = P(X_3 \le 22) = 0.9987$$

Path A-D-H-I: The analysis is exactly that same as the analysis for the previous path so
$$P(\text{A-D-H-I} \le 22 \text{ weeks}) = P(X_4 \le 22) = 0.9987$$

Now using Eq. (9.13) with $X = \max\{X_1, X_2, X_3, X_4\}$, we get

$$P(X \le 22) = 0.31 \times 1 \times 0.9987 \times 0.9987 \cong 0.31$$

(b) Applying the late start approach, generates a situation in which all paths are critical. Therefore, the probability that the project is completed within 22 weeks is

$$P(X \le 22 \text{ weeks}) = P(E \le 6 \text{ weeks}) \times P(D \le 7 \text{ weeks}) = 0.31 \times 0.5 = 0.155$$

The **assumptions** in both cases were (1) that each uncertain activity is normally distributed and (2) that their completion times are independent of each other.

CHAPTER

10. RESOURCE MANAGEMENT

10.1 We wish to develop a schedule that minimizes resource fluctuations. The CPM analysis for the project follows:

Activity	ES	EF	LS	LE	Resource hours/days	Slack
A	0	3	1	4	4	1
B	0	4	2	6	4	2
C	0	3	0	3	3	0
D	3	5	5	7	5	2
E	4	5	6	7	6	2
F	3	8	4	9	3	1
G	4	6	7	9	8	3
H	4	7	7	10	4	3
I	3	14	3	14	4	0
J	5	8	7	10	10	2
K	8	9	9	10	10	1
L	9	13	10	14	4	1
M	8	12	10	14	2	2

Project duration = 14 days
Total resource requirements = 204 hours
The average daily resource usage = 204/14 = 14.57 hours/day or between 14 and 15 hours.
The following table depicts a possible solution.

Day	A	B	C	D	E	F	G	H	I	J	K	L	M	Hours/day
1	4	4	3											11
2	4	4	3											11
3	4	4	3											11
4		4		5		3			4					16
5				5	6	3		4	4					22
6						3	8	4	4					19
7						3	8	4	4					19
8						3			4	10				17
9									4	10				14
10									4	10	10			24
11									4			4	2	10
12									4			4	2	10
13									4			4	2	10
14									4			4	2	10

10.2 (a) The two priority rules are:

1. Assign activities with smaller slack first
2. Assign activities with larger resource requirements first

The solution obtained by this procedure when the maximum availability is 24 – 2 = 22 hr/day is presented in the following tables:

	Activity													
Day	A	B	C	D	E	F	G	H	I	J	K	L	M	Hours/day
1	4	4	3											11
2	4	4	3											11
3	4	4	3											11
4		4		5		3			4					16
5				5	6	3		4	4					22
6						3	8	4	4					19
7						3	8	4	4					19
8						3			4	10				17
9									4	10				14
10									4	10				14
11									4		10		2	16
12									4			4	2	10
13									4			4	2	10
14									4			4	2	10
15												4		4

(b) In the solution is generated using both priority rules. Although the project takes one additional day, the maximum resource requirement is down to 22.

10.3 To solve the problem, daily requirements of each resource are (hours of resource type required per day) calculated along with the early start, late start, early finish, and late finish times of each activity.

Mode 1

Activity	ES	EF	LS	LF	Resource I (hrs/day)	Resource II (hrs/day)	Activity duration (days)
A	0	2	0	2	0	2.5	2
B	2	5	4	7	3	2	3
C	2	7	2	7	2	1	5
D	0	3	6	9	2	3	3
E	7	9	7	9	4	3	2
F	9	10	9	10	4	3	1

Mode 2

Activity	ES	EF	LS	LF	Resource I (hrs/day)	Resource II (hrs/day)	Activity duration (days)
A	0	1	0	1	12	7	1
B	1	3	3	5	6	4	2
C	1	5	1	5	4	4	4
D	0	2	4	6	3	4	2
E	5	6	5	6	9	5	1
F	6	7	6	7	4	3	1

Two different solutions are presented.

1. Objective is constant resource usage (all activities performed in mode I to save resources).

Day	Activities performed	Mode	Resource I (hours)	Resource II (hours)
1	A,D	1	2	5.5
2	A,D	1	2	5.5
3	C,D	1	4	4
4	B,C	1	5	3
5	B,C	1	5	3
6	B,C	1	5	3
7	C	1	2	1
8	D	1	4	3
9	D	1	4	3
10	E	1	4	3

2. Objective is to minimize the duration of the project: critical activities performed in mode 2, other activities in mode 1.

Day	Activity (mode)	Resource I (hours)	Resource II (hours)
1	A(2)	12	7
2	B(1), C(2), D(1)	9	9
3	B(1), C(2), D(1)	9	9
4	B(1), C(2), D(1)	9	9
5	C(2)	4	4
6	E(2)	9	5
7	F(2)	4	3

10.4 We assume that the following activities are required.

Activity	Description	Duration	Predecessor	Resource
A	Clean the passenger compartment	1 hr	–	Cleaner
B	Clean toilets × 6	5 min each	–	Cleaner
C	Unload empty food containers	30 min	–	Cleaner
D	Load food containers	15 min	C	Cleaner
E	Refuel	45 min	–	Technician
F	Maintenance operations	30 min	–	Technician
G	Tests	15 min	E, F	Technician
H	Fix problems	probabilistic	G	Technician

An early-start schedule is preferred for operations E, F, G and H because of the probabilistic nature of H which is critical. For the same reason the technicians are the bottleneck resource.

10.5 (a) and (b) The early start schedule is shown in the following table. The numbers indicate the crew size for the corresponding activity; those in bold are critical. For example, activity C is critical, it takes 6 weeks, and requires 3 crew members.

Week	A	B	C	D	E	F	G	H	I	J	No. of crew members
						Activity					
1	**4**					5					9
2	**4**					5					9
3	**4**							2			6
4	**4**							2			6
5		5	**3**					2			10
6		5	**3**					2			10
7			**3**	7				2			12
8			**3**	7				2			12
9			**3**	7				2			12
10			**3**				6			2	11
11					**6**		6			2	14
12					**6**		6			2	14
13					**6**		6			2	14
14					**6**		6			2	14
15					**6**					2	8
16					**6**					2	8
17					**6**					2	8
18					**6**					2	8
19					**6**					2	8
20					**6**						6
21									**8**		8

The late start schedule is as follows.

Week	A	B	C	D	E	F	G	H	I	J	No. of crew members
1	4										4
2	4										4
3	4					5					9
4	4					5					9
5			3					2			5
6			3					2			5
7			3					2			5
8			3					2			5
9			3					2			5
10			3					2			5
11		5			6			2			13
12		5			6				2		13
13				7	6				2		15
14				7	6				2		15
15				7	6				2		15
16					6		6		2		14
17					6		6		2		14
18					6		6		2		14
19					6		6		2		14
20					6		6		2		14
21									8	2	10

(c) Total person-weeks = 207. Because the project completion time is 21 weeks, a perfectly leveled schedule would mean $207/21 = 9.86 \cong 10$ crew members would be required to work each week. This value provides a good target.

Using the early-start schedule for the analysis, we see that the first time the crew size requirements exceed 10 is during the 7th week. In the first six weeks, the cumulative number of crew members required is only $9 + 9 + 6 + 6 + 10 + 10 = 50$, which gives an average of 8.33. In general, there is no reason to delay future activities as long as the average crew requirements are less than 10. The first time that the average exceeds 10 is during the 11th week (the average is $111/11 = 10.1$). At this point, we consider delaying one or more of the upcoming activities not on the critical path. The two candidates are the activities G and J. Because delaying G would create a large variance in future requirements, it is better to focus on J. If J is delayed two weeks, crew requirements are reduced by two during the 10th and 11th weeks, and increased by two during the 20th and 21st weeks. As a result, we have a more leveled scheduled with a minimum requirement of 8 instead of 6 towards the end of the project

10.6 (a) With a limit of 10 crew members per day under the stated assumption and conditions, we get the following schedule and labor utilization.

Week	A	B	C	D	E	F	G	H	I	J	No. of crew members
1	4					5					9
2	4					5					9
3	4							2			6
4	4							2			6
5		5	3					2			10
6		5	3					2			10
7			3					2			5
8			3					2			5
9			3					2			5
10			3						2		5
11					6				2		8
12					6				2		8
13					6				2		8
14					6				2		8
15					6				2		8
16					6				2		8
17					6				2		8
18					6				2		8
19					6				2		8
20					6						6
21				7							7
22				7							7
23				7							7
24							6				6
25							6				6
26							6				6
27							6				6
28							6				6
29										8	8

(b) Solution when it is possible to reduce the crew size and increase its duration (the number of person-weeks required for each activity is constant).

Week	A	B	C	D	E	F	G	H	I	J	No. of crew members
1	4					5					9
2	4					5					9
3	4							2			6
4	4							2			6
5		5	3					2			10
6		5	3					2			10
7			3					2			5
8			3					2			5
9			3					2			5
10			3						2		5
11					6		2		2		10
12					6		2		2		10
13					6		2		2		10
14					6		2		2		10
15					6		2		2		10
16					6		2		2		10
17					6		2		2		10
18					6		2		2		10
19					6		2		2		10
20					6		2				8
21				7			2				9
				7			2				9
				7			2				9
							2				2
							2				2
										8	8

(c) Because activity splitting cannot reduce the duration any further, the solution is the same as in part (b).

10.7 Assuming a symmetric trapezoid profile for each activity, using the equation

$$lbrq = peak \times \left(\frac{dur}{2} + 0.5\right)$$

where lbrq = total labor required to perform the activity
  peak = peak labor required during the one week peak time
  dur = activity duration.

the peak labor required during the one week peak time for each activity is calculated and shown in the last column of the following table:

Activity	Duration	Labor requirement	Peak
A	4	16	6.4
B	2	10	6.7
C	6	18	5.1
D	3	21	10.5
E	10	60	10.9
F	2	10	6.7
G	5	30	10.0
H	7	14	3.5
I	1	8	8.0
J	10	20	3.6

10.8 Using the following notation:

UTIL = crew utilization for an activity
T = duration of peak resource requirements
P = peak resource requirements
D = activity duration

the crew utilization for an activity is

$$UTIL = (T \times P + [(D - T)/2]P)/(D \times P) = (D + T)/2D$$

10.9   (a) The second project is identical to the one described in Exercise 10.5 and is scheduled to start one week after the first. To generate its profile, the same profile used in 10-5(a) should be added to itself with one week delay, as follows:

Week	Project 1	Project 2	Total crew members
1	9		9
2	9	9	18
3	6	9	15
4	6	6	12
5	10	6	16
6	10	10	20
7	12	10	22
8	12	12	24
9	12	12	24
10	11	12	23
11	14	11	25
12	14	14	28
13	14	14	28
14	14	14	28
15	8	14	22
16	8	8	16
17	8	8	16
18	8	8	16
19	8	8	16
20	6	8	14
21	8	6	14
22		8	8

(b) The two projects required $207 \times 2 = 414$ person-weeks during a period of 22 weeks. This gives an average of $414/22 = 18.8 \cong 19$. Because activity G starts at week 10 and has a slack of 6 weeks, it may be delayed by 6 weeks in project 1. After introducing this delay, the new profile has the following values:

Week	Total crew members
1	9
2	18
3	15
4	12
5	16
6	20
7	22
8	24
9	24
10	17
11	19
12	22
13	22
14	22
15	16
16	22
17	22
18	22
19	22
20	20
21	20
22	8

This shift in schedule reduces the peak from 28 to 22 crew members.

(c) The peak reduction from 28 to 22 has a significant impact on labor cost. Through this exercise one may observe the benefits that may arise from multiproject scheduling.

10.10 Let us make the following assumptions:

1. The time to complete the activity and the corresponding labor requirements are both normally distributed
2. Activity complete time and labor requirements are independent of each other

(a) Let T be a random variable associated with the completion time of the activity and let L be a random variable associated with the labor requirements. The probability of completing the activity within its mean (i.e., less than or equal to 10 days) is

$$P(T \leq 10) = 0.5$$

A 10% addition to labor-days means a total of 33 labor-days. The corresponding Z value is

$$Z = \frac{33-30}{3} = 1$$

The probability that the required labor-days will be at least 33 is

$$P(L \geq 33) = P(Z \geq 1) = 0.16$$

Because of the independence assumption, the joint probability is

$$P(T \leq 10,\ L \geq 33) = P(T \leq 10)P(L \geq 33) = (0.5)(0.16) = 0.08$$

(b) In addition to the above assumptions, it is assumed that the three workers are treated as single unit. Consequently, the expected labor requirements for the activity are 10 unit-days with a standard deviation of 1 unit-day. The probability of completion in no more than 11 days is equivalent to the probability that no more than 11 unit-days will be needed. Letting U be a random variable associated with unit days, we have

$$P(U \leq 11) = 1 - P(L \geq 33) = 1 - 0.16 = 0.84$$

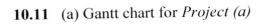

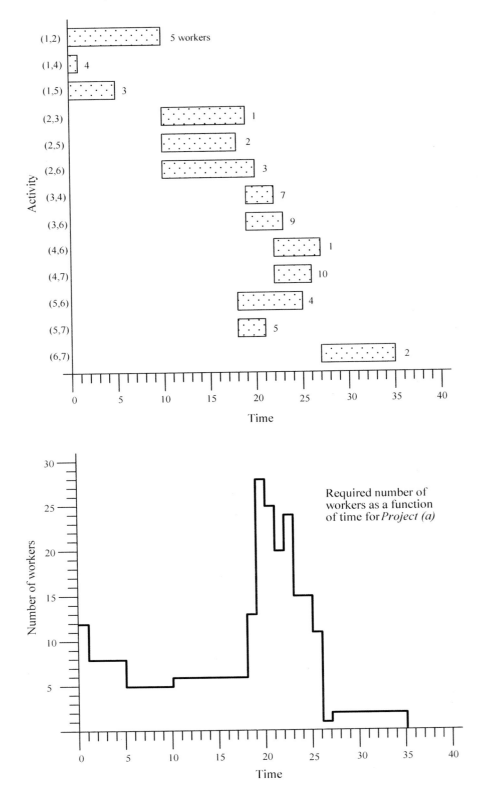

10.11 (a) Gantt chart for *Project (a)*

Gantt chart for *Project (b)*

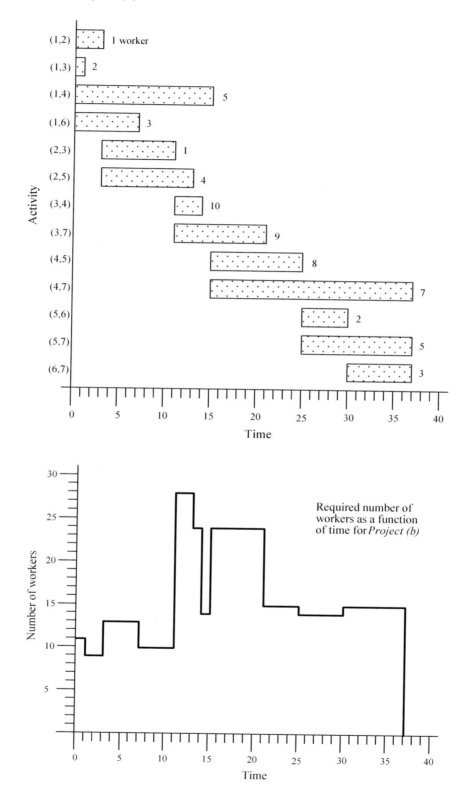

10.11 (b) Level schedule Gantt chart for *Project (a)*

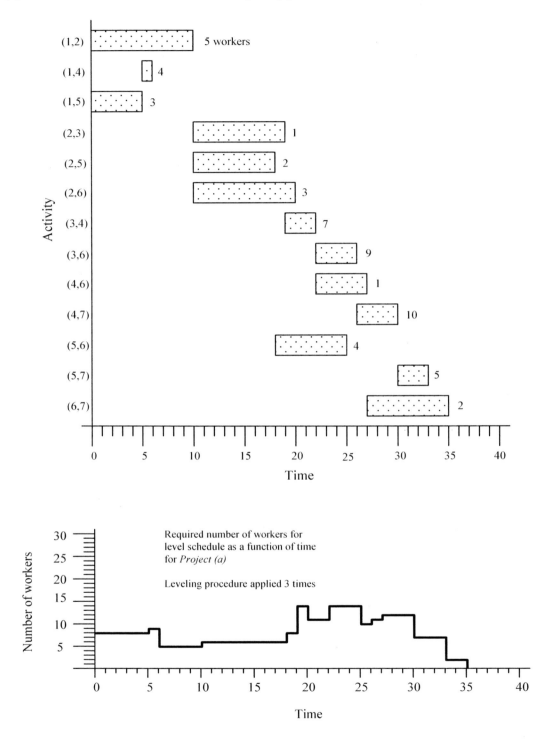

Level schedule Gantt chart for *Project (b)*

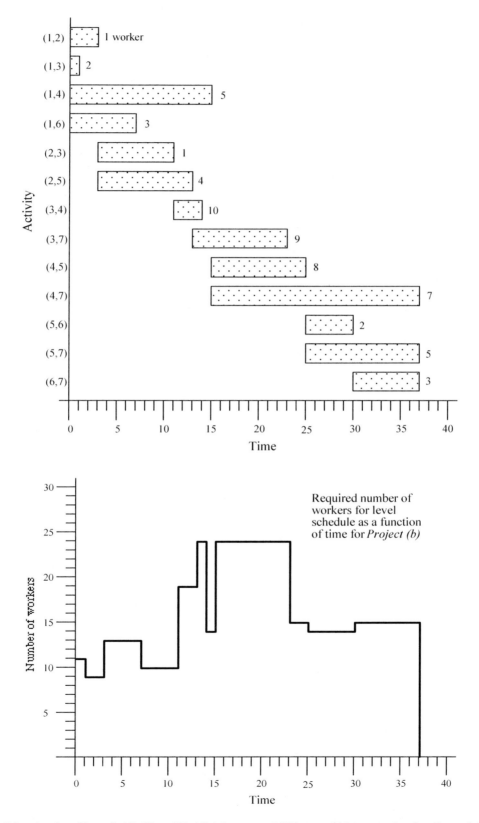

Required number of workers for level schedule as a function of time for *Project (b)*

10.12 (a) *Precedence graph*

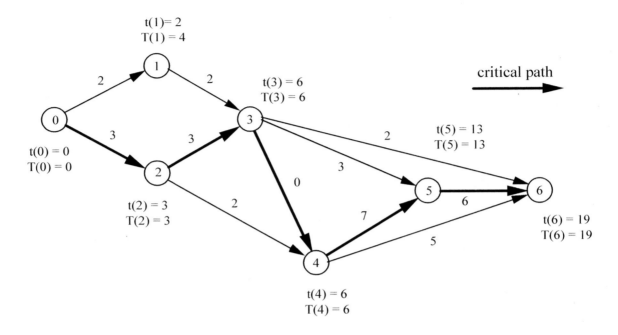

(b)

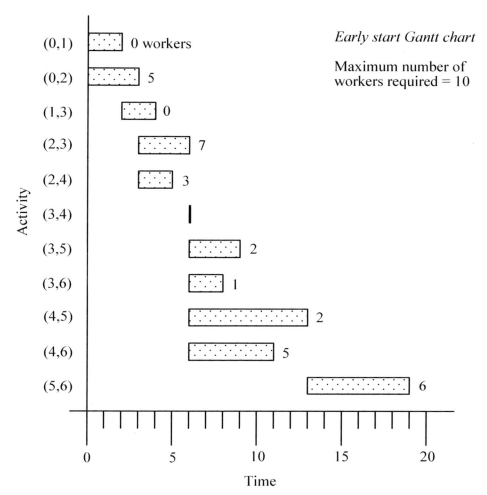

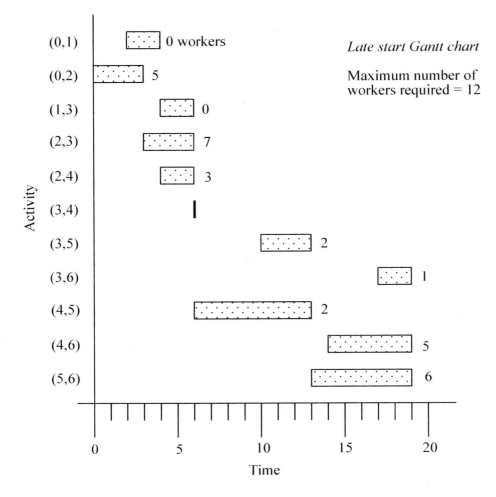

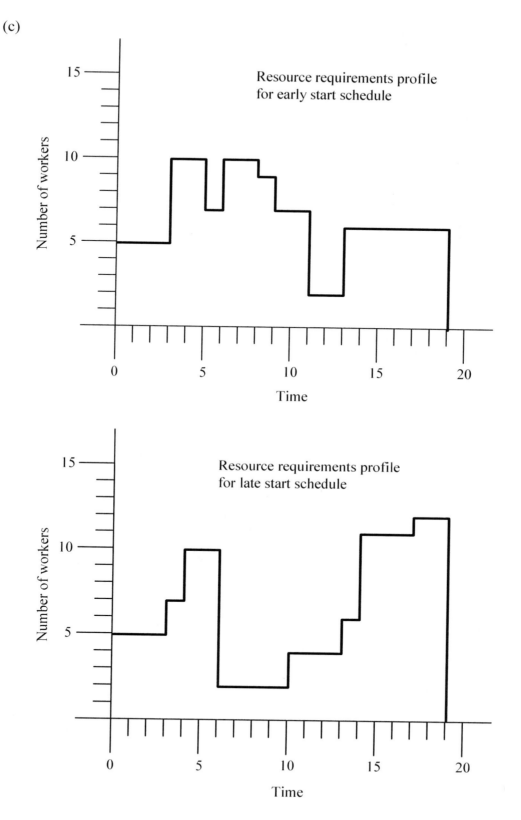

(c)

(d)

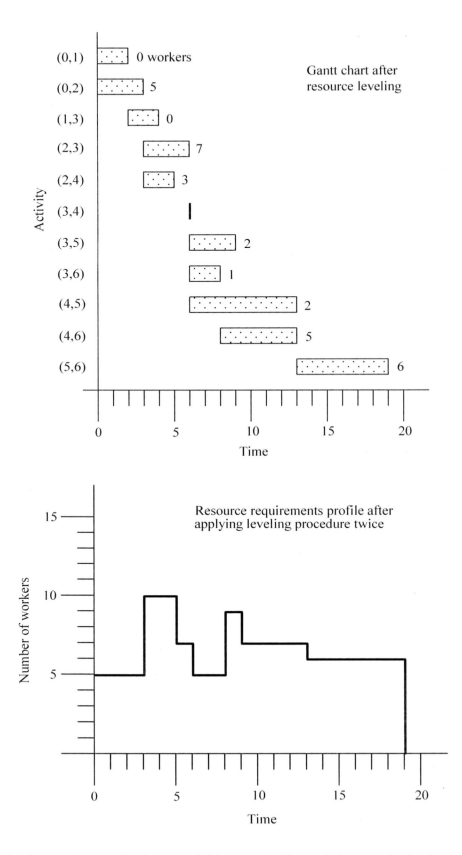

(e)

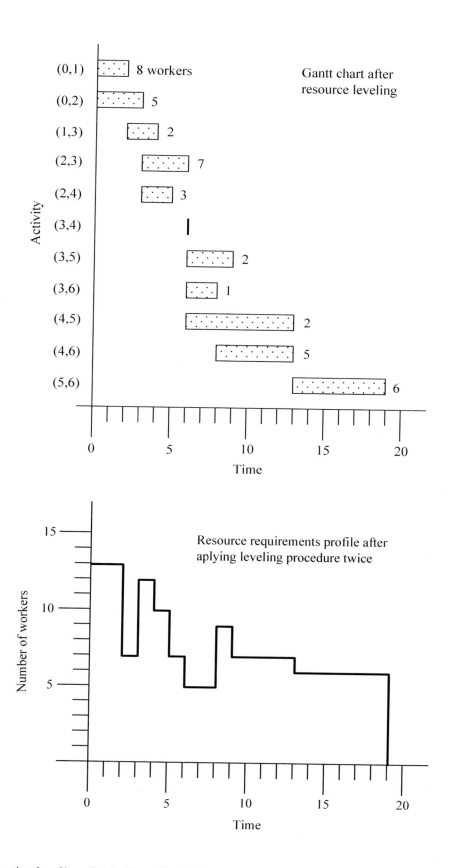

10.13 (a) This exercise is structured differently (but more realistically) from the approach in the text in order to stimulate critical thinking rather than duplication.

First, we solve the problem by ignoring the available supply of personnel.

Activity	(i,j)	d_{ij}	E_i	L_j	TS_{ij}	FS_{ij}
A	(1,2)	10	0	10	0	0
B	(2,4)	8	10	18	0	0
D_1	(2,3)	0	10	18	8	0
C	(3,5)	5	10	23	8	0
D	(4,6)	6	18	24	0	0
E	(6,8)	8	24	32	0	0
F	(5,7)	7	15	30	8	0
D_2	(7,8)	0	22	32	10	10
D_3	(7,9)	0	22	31	9	0
D_4	(7,10)	0	22	30	8	0
G	(8,12)	4	32	36	0	0
H	(9,11)	2	22	33	9	1
I	(10,11)	3	22	33	8	0
J	(11,12)	3	25	36	8	8
K	(12,13)	2	36	38	0	0

Critical path: A-B-D-E-G-K or 1-2-4-6-8-12-13

Earliest completion time: 38 person-days

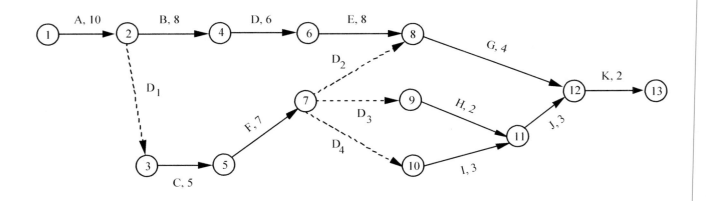

(b)

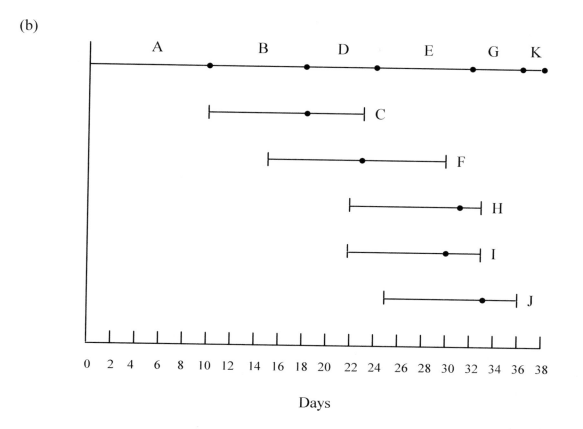

Days

From the Gantt chart, it can be seen that more than 5 persons are never needed regardless of when noncritical activities are scheduled, as long as each activity utilizes one and only one person (i.e., if you draw a vertical line at any point, then at most it intersects 5 activities).

(c) Now, we allow the assignment of one to five persons to each activity. On any given day, a maximum of five persons can be assigned to all activities that are active for that day. The heuristic assignment table below minimizes the completion time for the project.

For example, on day 1, five persons are assigned to activity A. Five person-days of work remain for A, and the longest path to event 13 is still A-B-D-E-G-K. The assignment in day 2 completes activity A and leaves B-D-E-G-K as the critical path. Note that three persons are assigned to B in day 4 because B is on the critical path. This assignment completes B by the end of day 4, which means that D cannot be started until day 5. Because two people remain unassigned in day 4 we assign them to C, an activity currently off the critical path.

Day	Assignment	Person-days remaining for assigned activity	Remaining critical path(s)	Number of persons assigned
1	5 to A	5	A-B-D-E-G-K	5
2	5 to A	0	B-D-E-G-K	5
3	5 to B	3	B-D-E-G-K	5
4	3 to B	0		
	2 to C	3	D-E-G-K	5
5	5 to D	1	$C-F-D_4-I-J-K$	5
6	3 to C	0		
	2 to F	5	D-E-G-K	5
7	1 to D	0		
	4 to E	4	$F-D_4-I-J-K$	5
8	5 to F	0	E-G-K	5
9	4 to E	0	H-J-K	
	1 to I	2	I-J-K	5
10	2 to H	0		
	2 to I	0	G-K	
	1 to G	3	J-K	5
11	3 to G	0		
	2 to J	1	J-K	5
12	1 to J	0	—	5
	2 to K	0		3

Note that the heuristic calls for assigning as many people as possible to the first critical activity not yet completed. Once this assignment is made, any remaining persons can be assigned to the next noncritical activity. Also note that the day's assignment usually changes the critical path. The assignments in the table yield a minimum completion time for the project of 12 days.

(d) Here it depends on what is meant by "best balance." If we wish to minimize the standard deviation of "number of persons assigned per day" (the last column in the table), then it can be done by assigning, say, one person each day until the project is completed. This would give a standard deviation of zero and a completion date of 38 days. If we wish to minimize the unemployment rate, then the assignments in the table accomplish this.

(e) If there are unlimited personnel, the project could be compressed 6 days to a length of 6.

Day	Assignment	Person-days remaining for assigned activity	Remaining critical path(s)	Number of persons assigned
1	10 to A	0		
	5 to C	0	B-D-E-G-K	15
2	8 to B	0		
	7 to F	0	D-E-G-K	15
3	6 to D	0		
	2 to H	0		
	3 to I	0	E-G-K	11
4	8 to E	0		
	3 to J	0	G-K	11
5	4 to G	0	K	4
6	2 to K	0	—	2

CHAPTER

11. PROJECT BUDGET

11.1

(a) The total cost of the project is $62,000. An early start budget follows.

Days	A	B	C	D	E	F	G	H	I	J	K	L	M	Daily cost	Cumulative cost
1	1000	500	2000											3500	$3,500
2	1000	500	2000											3500	$7,000
3	1000	500	2000											3500	$10,500
4		500		1000		2000			1000					4500	$15,000
5				1000	1000	2000	2000	3000	1000					10000	$25,000
6						2000	2000	3000	1000	1000				9000	$34,000
7						2000		3000	1000	1000				7000	$41,000
8						2000			1000	1000				4000	$45,000
9									1000		1000		2000	4000	$49,000
10									1000			500	2000	3500	$52,500
11									1000			500	2000	3500	$56,000
12									1000			500	2000	3500	$59,500
13									1000			500		1500	$61,000
14									1000					1000	$62,000
Total	3000	2000	6000	2000	1000	10000	4000	9000	11000	3000	1000	2000	8000		

(b) Late-start budget

Activity

Days	A	B	C	D	E	F	G	H	I	J	K	L	M	Daily cost	Cumulative cost
1			2000											2000	$2,000
2	1000		2000											3000	$5,000
3	1000	500	2000											3500	$8,500
4	1000	500							1000					2500	$11,000
5		500				2000			1000					3500	$14,500
6		500		1000		2000			1000					4500	$19,000
7				1000	1000	2000			1000					5000	$24,000
8						2000	2000	3000	1000	1000				9000	$33,000
9						2000	2000	3000	1000	1000				9000	$42,000
10								3000	1000	1000	1000			6000	$48,000
11									1000			500	2000	3500	$51,500
12									1000			500	2000	3500	$55,000
13									1000			500	2000	3500	$58,500
14									1000			500	2000	3500	$62,000
Total	3000	2000	6000	2000	1000	10000	4000	9000	11000	3000	1000	2000	8000		

(c) The total cost of the project is $62,000 and its duration is 14 days. Assuming a perfectly leveled budget, the daily cost should be about $4,428 (= $62,000/14). The following is one possible solution:

Days	A	B	C	D	E	F	G	H	I	J	K	L	M	Daily cost	Cumulative cost
1	1000	500	2000											3500	$3,500
2	1000	500	2000											3500	$7,000
3	1000	500	2000											3500	$10,500
4		500		1000		2000			1000					4500	$15,000
5				1000	1000	2000		3000	1000					8000	$23,000
6						2000	2000	3000	1000					8000	$31,000
7						2000	2000	3000	1000					8000	$39,000
8						2000			1000	1000				4000	$43,000
9									1000	1000	1000			3000	$46,000
10									1000	1000		500		2500	$48,500
11									1000			500	2000	3500	$52,000
12									1000			500	2000	3500	$55,500
13									1000			500	**2000**	3000	$59,000
14									1000				2000	3000	$62,000
Total	3000	2000	6000	2000	1000	10000	4000	9000	11000	3000	1000	2000	8000		

Activity

11.2 To develop the functional relationship between the direct cost of the project and its duration we start with a schedule in which each activity is performed in normal time (and normal or minimum direct cost). The duration of the project is shortened by using an algorithm that at each step, the activity(ies) that are the least expensive to crash (and are critical) are crashed. This procedure gives the following solution.

Project duration	Activity to crash	New activity duration	Cost to crash	Project total direct cost
14	–	–	–	$62,000
13	C	2	$500	$62,500
12	I	10	$1,500	
	F	4	$500	$64,500
11	I	9	$1,500	
	L	3	$1,000	$67,000
10	I	8	$1,500	
	A	2	$1,000	
	B	3	$1,000	$70,500

Based on this solution, we have the following functional relationship between the direct cost of the project and its duration.

Project duration	Project total direct cost
14	$62,000
13	$62,500
12	$64,500
11	$67,000
10	$70,500

11.3

a) Overhead = $2,000 + $1,000 × duration

Project duration	Cost of crashing	Overhead	Total cost
14	0	$16,000	$16,000
13	$500	$15,000	$15,500
12	$2,500	$14,000	$16,500
11	$5,000	$13,000	$18,000
10	$8,500	$12,000	$20,500

For example, if we crash to 13 days, then the total cost is $15,500.

b) Overhead = \$2000 + \$3000 × duration

Project duration	Cost of crashing	Overhead	Total cost
14	0	\$44,000	\$44,000
13	\$500	\$41,000	\$41,500
12	\$2,500	\$38,000	\$40,500
11	\$5,000	\$35,000	\$40,000
10	\$8,500	\$32,000	\$40,500

For example, if we crash to 11days, then the total cost is \$40,000.

11.4 Notation for AOA model

(i,j) activity that starts at node i and ends at node j
A set of activities
n index for end node

Parameters
NT_{ij} normal time of activity (i,j)
CT_{ij} crash time of activity (i,j)
T required project completion time
NC_{ij} normal cost for activity (i,j)
CC_{ij} crash cost for activity (i,j)
C_o overhead cost per time unit

Variables
t_j time of event j
X_{ij} duration of activity (i,j)

Computed coefficient

$$C_{ij} = \frac{CC_{ij} - NC_{ij}}{NT_{ij} - CT_{ij}} = \text{crashing cost per time unit}$$

The cost of activity (i,j) if its duration is X_{ij} time units: $NC_{ij} + C_{ij}(NT_{ij} - X_{ij})$.

Model

$$\text{Minimize}\left\{C_o t_n + \sum_{(i,j)\in A}\left(NC_{ij} + C_{ij}NT_{ij} - C_{ij}X_{ij}\right)\right\}$$

or

$$\text{Minimize}\left\{C_o t_n - \sum_{(i,j)\in A} C_{ij}X_{ij}\right\} + \sum_{(i,j)\in A}\left(NC_{ij} + C_{ij}NT_{ij}\right)$$

$$\text{subject to} \quad CT_{ij} \le X_{ij} \le NT_{ij} \quad \forall (i,j) \in A$$

$$t_j - t_i \ge X_{ij} \quad \forall (i,j) \in A$$

$$t_n \le T$$

$$t_1 \ge 0$$

11.5   The early-start and late-start normal time schedules are:

Activity	ES	EF	LS	LF
A	0	4	0	4
B	0	3	1	4
C	4	6	5	7
D	4	7	4	7
E	4	8	5	9
F	7	11	7	11
G	8	10	9	11
H	11	14	11	14

Both schedules take 14 weeks. The critical activities, total slack, and free slack of each activity are given in the following table.

Activity	Critical	Free slack (weeks)	Total slack (weeks)
A	yes	0	0
B	no	1	1
C	no	1	1
D	yes	0	0
E	yes	0	1
F	yes	0	0
G	no	1	1
H	yes	0	0

The cost of the early-start and late-start schedules with all activities performed in normal time is:

Direct cost of activities = $100 + $200 + $50 + $100 + $150 + $250 + $300 + $200

= $1,350

The overhead for 14 weeks is $350 × 14 = $4,900

The total cost = $13,350 + $4,900 = $6,250

By crashing activities A, F, G, H at the additional direct cost of $100 + $300 + $100 + $200 = $700, the duration is reduced to 9 weeks and the total cost is reduced to

$6,250 + $700 − $350 × 5 = $5,200

Based on the early-start schedule, the linear program and its solution follow:

Week	A	B	C (A,B)	D (A,B)	E (A)	F (C,D)	G (D,E)	H (F,G)	Overhead cost	Weekly cost	Cumulative cost
						Activity					
1	25	67							350	442	442
2	25	67							350	442	883
3	25	67							350	442	1325
4	25								350	375	1700
5			25	33	38				350	446	2146
6			25	33	38				350	446	2592
7				33	38				350	421	3013
8					38	63			350	450	3463
9						63	150		350	563	4025
10						63	150		350	563	4588
11						63			350	413	5000
12								67	350	417	5417
13								67	350	417	5833
14								67	350	417	6250
Total activity cost	100	200	50	100	150	250	300	200	4900	6250	
Duration	4	3	2	3	4	4	2	3			
Crash time	2	1	1	2	1	1	1	2			
Crash cost	300	200	100	300	400	100	200	100			

By shortening the critical path we save $350/period of overhead cost. However, we must also take into account crashing cost. Assuming that a continuous time-cost tradeoff exists for each activity, by carefully crashing the activities on the critical path, we get:

	A	B	C (A,B)	D (A,B)	E (A)	F (C,D)	G(D,E)	H(F,G)			
1	50	100							350	500	500
2	50	100							350	500	1000
3			25	33	50				350	458	1458
4			25	33	50				350	458	1917
5				33	50				350	433	2350
6						250	300		350	900	3250
7								100	350	450	3700
8								100	350	450	4150
9										0	4150
10										0	4150
11										0	4150
12										0	4150
13										0	4150
14										0	4150
Total activity cost	100	200	50	100	150	250	300	200	2800	4150	
True duration	2	2	2	3	3	1	1	2			
Duration	4	3	2	3	4	4	2	3			
Crash time	2	1	1	2	1	1	1	2			
Crash cost	300	200	100	300	400	100	200	100			

Crash cost /week	150	100	100	300	133	33	200	100		Critical paths
14									6250	ADFH
13						33			5933	ADFH, AEGH
12								100	5683	ADFH, AEGH
11	150								5483	ADFH, BDFH, AEGH
10					133	33			5299	AEGH, ADGH, BDGH, ADFH, BDFH
9						33	200		5182	AEGH, ADGH, BDGH, ADFH, BDFH
8	150	100						BEST	5082	AEGH, ADGH, BDGH, ADFH, BDFH
7				300	133				5165	AEGH, ADGH, BDGH, ADFH, BDFH

The calculations for each crashed week were done by taking the previous week, adding the cost of crashing, and subtracting the $350 overhead cost. From the table above, we see that when week 7 is crashed, the cost is $433 which is more then the 350$ overhead cost saving.

In weeks 12 and 13, it was more advantageous to crash activities that were on both critical paths (A and H) rather then to crash the less expensive separate activities (like E & F).

Final critical activities: ADFH, ADGH, AEGH, BDFH and BDGH
The only noncritical activity left is C (1 week). We still have reserves to crash activities B(1), C(1), D(1) and E(2).

Late-start chart:

Week	A	B	C (A,B)	D (A,B)	E (A)	F (C,D)	G (D,E)	H (F,G)	Overhead cost	Weekly cost	Cumulative
1	25								350	375	375
2	25	67							350	442	817
3	25	67							350	442	1258
4	25	67							350	442	1700
5				33					350	383	2083
6			25	33	38				350	446	2529
7			25	33	38				350	446	2975
8					38	63			350	450	3425
9					38	63			350	450	3875
10						63	150		350	563	4437
11						63	150		350	563	5000
12								67	350	417	5416
13								67	350	417	5833
14								67	350	417	6250
Total activity cost	100	200	50	100	150	250	300	200	4900	6250	
Duration	4	3	2	3	4	4	2	3			
Crash time	2	1	1	2	1	1	1	2			
Crash cost	300	200	100	300	400	100	200	100			

Excel table for optimizing with Solver:

	Activity		Time (weeks)		Cost		Max time reduction	Crash cost/week	Start time	Time reduction	Finish time
			normal	crash	normal	crash					
	A		4	2	100	400	2	150	0	0	4
	B		3	1	200	400	2	100	0	0	3
	C	AB	2	1	50	150	1	100	4	0	6
	D	AB	3	2	100	400	1	300	4	0	7
	E	A	4	1	150	550	3	133	4	0	8
	F	CD	4	1	250	350	3	33	7	0	11
	G	DE	2	1	300	500	1	200	8	0	10
	H	FG	3	2	200	300	1	100	11	0	14

max finish time (cell F14)	9
total cost (cell F16)	4500

Formulas used:

A	B Activity	C	D Time (weeks) normal	E Time (weeks) crash	F Cost normal	G Cost crash	H Max time reduction	I Crash cost/week	J Start time	K Time reduction	L Finish time	Added cost to crash
2	Activity		Time (weeks)		Cost		Max time reduction	Crash cost/week	Start time	Time reduction	Finish time	Added cost to crash
3			normal	crash	normal	crash						
4	A		4	2	100	=N4+F4	=D4-E4	=(G4-F4)/H4	0	0	=J4+D4-K4	300
5	B		3	1	200	=N5+F5	=D5-E5	=(G5-F5)/H5	0	0	=J5+D5-K5	200
6	C	AB	2	1	50	=N6+F6	=D6-E6	=(G6-F6)/H6	4	0	=J6+D6-K6	100
7	D	AB	3	2	100	=N7+F7	=D7-E7	=(G7-F7)/H7	4	0	=J7+D7-K7	300
8	E	A	4	1	150	=N8+F8	=D8-E8	=(G8-F8)/H8	4	0	=J8+D8-K8	400
9	F	CD	4	1	250	=N9+F9	=D9-E9	=(G9-F9)/H9	7	0	=J9+D9-K9	100
10	G	DE	2	1	300	=N10+F10	=D10-E10	=(G10-F10)/H10	8	0	=J10+D10-K10	200
11	H	FG	3	2	200	=N11+F11	=D11-E11	=(G11-F11)/H11	11	0	=J11+D11-K11	100
12												
13												
14			max finish time	9								
15												
16			total cost	=SUM(F4:F11)+SUMPRODUCT(I4:I11,K4:K11)+350*F14								
17												

The solver used:

        Set target cell:F16

        Equal to: min

        By changing cells: J4:K11

        Constraints:

$J6 \geq L4$,	$J10 \geq L7$
$J6 \geq L5$,	$J10 \geq L8$
$J7 \geq L4$,	$J11 \geq L9$
$J7 \geq L5$,	$J11 \geq L10$
$J8 \geq L4$,	$F14 \leq 9$
$J9 \geq L6$,	$F14 \geq L11$
$J9 \geq L7$,	$K4:K11 \leq H4:H11$

Results:

A	B	C	D	E	F	G	H	I	J	K	L
2	Activity		Time (weeks)		Cost		Max time reduction	Crash cost/week	Start time	Time reduction	Finish time
3			normal	crash	normal	crash					
4	A		4	2	100	400	2	150	0	1	3
5	B		3	1	200	400	2	100	0	1.51E-10	3
6	C	AB	2	1	50	150	1	100	4	0	6
7	D	AB	3	2	100	400	1	300	3	0	6
8	E	A	4	1	150	550	3	133	3	1	6
9	F	CD	4	1	250	350	3	33	6	3	7
10	G	DE	2	1	300	500	1	200	6	1	7
11	H	FG	3	2	200	300	1	100	7	1	9

11.6 Project *a*:

Activity	(1,2)	(1,4)	(1,5)	(2,3)	(2,5)	(2,6)	(3,4)	(3,6)	(4,6)	(4,7)	(5,6)	(5,7)	(6,7)
Slope	33.33	30.00	30.00	25.00	6.67	10.00	10.00	7.50	3.33	5.00	10.00	10.00	20.00

I Normal schedule: Time = 25; Cost = $1,150; Critical path (1,2,3,6,7)

II Compress (3,6): slope = 7.5; Crash limit = 4; FF-limit = 1; Compression limit = 1; Time = 24; Cost = $1,150 + $7.5 = $1,157.5; Critical paths: (1,2,3,6,7) & (1,2,3,4,7)

III Compress (3,6) & (4,7): slope = 7.5 + 5 = 12.5; Crash limit = min{3,4} = 3 FF-limit = 1; Compression limit = 1; Time = 23; Cost = $1,157.5 + $12.5 = $1,170; Critical paths: (1,2,3,6,7), (1,2,3,4,7) & (1,2,3,4,6 7)

IV Compress (3,6) (4,6), (4,7): slope = 7.50 + 3.33 + 5.00 = 15.83; Crash limit = min{2,3} = 2; FF-limit = 5; Compression limit = 2; Time = 21; Cost = $1,170 + $15.83 × 2 = $1,201.66; Critical path: (1,2,3,6,7)

V (3,6) has reached its crash limit possibilities for compression
  a) Compress (1,2): slope = 33.33
  b) Compress (2,3): slope = 25
  c) Compress (3,4) & (6,7) and expand (4,6): slope = 10 + 20 − 3.33 = 26.67
  d) Compress (6,7) and (4,7): slope = 20 + 5 = 25

Because (b) and (d) have the same slopes, both are carried out simultaneously; Crash limit = 2 + 1 = 3; FF-limit = 4; Compression limit = 3; Time = 18; Cost = $1,201.66 + 3 × $25 = $1,276.66; Critical paths: (1,2,3,6,7); (1,2,3,4,7) & (1,2,3,4,6,7)

VI Now, (2,3) and (4,6) are at crash limit; compress (3,4) and (6,7) and expand (4,6); Crash limit = min{2,3} = 1; Expansion limit = 2; Compression limit = 1; Time = 17; Cost = $1,276.66 + 1 × $26.67 = $1,303.33; Critical paths: (1,2,3,6,7); (1,2,3,4,7) & (1,2,3,4,6,7)

VII (6,7) at crash limit; Compress (1,2): slope = 33.33; Crash limit = 3; FF-limit = 7; Compression = 3; Cost = $1,203.33 + 3 × $33.33 = $1,403.33; Critical paths: (1,2,3,6,7); (1,2,3,4,6,7) & (1,2,3,4,7)

VIII Because all activities on the critical path (1,2,3,6,7) are at their crash limit, (1,2) is at its crash limit. This implies that no further compression is possible.

Summary

Duration	Cost
25	$1,150 → normal
24	$1,157.5
23	$1,170
21	$1,201.66
18	$1,276.66
17	$1,303.33
14	$1,403.33 → Crash

11.7 AOA diagram below. Information on each arrow includes (activity, normal time, crash time).

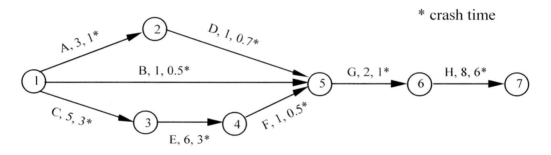

(a)

Step	Action	Critical path(s)	(Direct cost, Duration)
Normal	-	C-E-F-G-H	(140.9, 22)
All Crash	-	Same	(244.0, 13.5)
1	Crash F	Same	(141.7, 21.5)
2	Compress C	Same	(146.2, 20.5)
3	Crash C	Same	(150.7, 19.5)
4	Crash G	Same	(155.7, 18.5)
5	Compress E	Same	(165.7, 17.5)
6	Compress E	Same	(175.7, 16.5)
7	Crash E	Same	(185.7, 15.5)
8	Compress H	Same	(210.7, 14.5)
9	Crash H	Same	(235.7, 13.5)

Duration (weeks)	Direct cost	Indirect cost	Opportunity cost	Total
22	140.9	27.5	11.0	179.4
21.5	141.7	26.5	9.0	177.2
20.5	146.2	25.5	7.0	178.7
19.5	150.7	24.5	5.0	180.2
18.5	155.7	23.5	3.0	182.2
17.5	165.7	22.5	1.0	189.2
16.5	175.7	21.5	0	197.2
15.5	185.7	20.5	0	206.2
14.5	210.7	19.5	0	230.2
13.5	235.7	18.5	0	254.2

The duration for minimum total cost is 21.5 weeks. The time chart is the same as that in Exercise 7.19d, except that: activity F lasts 0.5 weeks instead of one week; the project ends by the end of week 21.5; latest finishing times for A, B, and D are 10.5, 11.5, and 11.5, respectively; and latest starting times for A, B, and D are each 0.5 weeks earlier (that is, each dot is moved 0.5 week to the left in the Gantt chart).

(b) Note, for example, that the cost of H is $100,000 for the normal time of 8 weeks; hence, assuming linearity, H costs $12,500 per week. In the following graph, direct costs are expressed on a weekly basis, rather than on a one-half week basis.

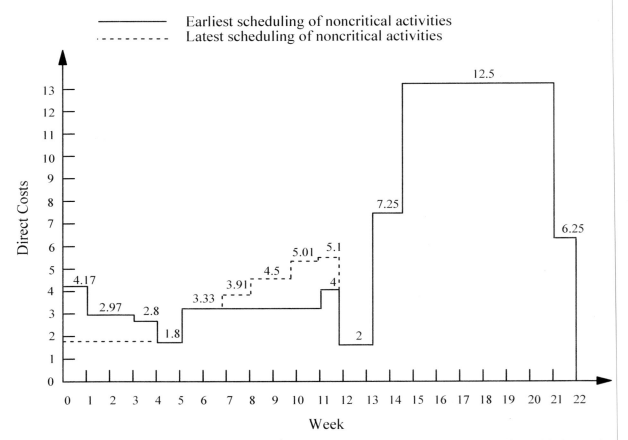

Both schedules have the same maximum cost of $12,500 for weeks 15 through 21. Moreover, both schedules result in an average requirement of $6,444 per week, but the earliest schedule does a slightly better job of smoothing funds based on variance. This is shown in the following table.

Week	Direct costs	
	Earliest schedule	Latest schedule
1	4.17	1.80
2	2.97	
3	2.97	
4	2.80	
5	1.80	1.80
6	3.33	3.33
7		3.33
8		3.91
9		4.50
10		4.50
11	3.33	5.01[4]
12	4.00[1]	5.10
13	2.00	2.00
14	7.25	7.25
15	12.50	12.50
16		
17		
18		
19		
20		
21	12.50	12.50
22	6.25[2]	6.25
Total	141.69[3]	141.68
Mean	6.44	6.44
Variance	19.31	20.11
Std. Dev.	4.39	4.46

[1] $3,000 for F in the first half of the twelfth week and $1,000 for G in the second half of the 12th week.

[2] $6,250 for completion of H in the first half of the 22nd week.

[3] Note that the totals are consistent with the previous time-cost schedule.

[4] $3,330 (1 week of E) + $580 (½ week of A) + $600 (½ week of B) + (½ week of D).

11.8 Crashing with penalty for project tardiness.

Notation

(i,j) activity that starts at node i and finishes at node j

A set of activities

Parameters

CC_{ij} crashing cost for activity (i,j)

NC_{ij} normal cost for activity (i,j)

CT_{ij} crashing time for activity (i,j)

NT_{ij} normal time for activity (i,j)

$C_{ij} = \dfrac{CC_{ij} - NC_{ij}}{NT_{ij} - CT_{ij}}$, crashing cost for activity (i,j) per time unit

T due date

C_o indirect variable cost

C_p penalty per one time unit of tardiness

F indirect fixed cost

Decision variables

x_{ij} duration of activity (i,j)

t_i time for event i (n is terminal event)

y length of project delay beyond T

If the duration of activity (i,j) is x_{ij} time units, then its cost is $NC_{ij} + C_{ij}(NT_{ij} - x_{ij})$. The full mixed-integer linear programming formulation follows.

Model

$$\text{Minimize} \left\{ \sum_{(i,j)\in A} \left(NC_{ij} + C_{ij}NT_{ij} - C_{ij}x_{ij} \right) + C_o t_n + F + C_p y \right\}$$

or

$$\text{Minimize} \left\{ C_o t_n - \sum_{(i,j)\in A} C_{ij}x_{ij} + C_p y \right\} + \sum_{(i,j)\in A} \left(NC_{ij} + C_{ij}NT_{ij} \right) + F \quad (1a)$$

$$\text{subject to} \quad CT_{ij} \le x_{ij} \le NT_{ij} \quad \forall\, (i,j)\in A \quad (1b)$$

$$t_j - t_i \ge x_{ij} \quad \forall\, (i,j)\in A \quad (1c)$$

$$y \ge t_n - T,\ y \ge 0 \quad (1d)$$

$$t_1 \ge 0 \quad (1e)$$

Note that the term on the right in the objective function (1a) is a constant and is not included in the solution below.

Excel solution

	A	B	C	D	E	F	G	H	I
1	activity	(i,j)	normal time	crash time	direct normal cost	direct crash cost	Cij	Xij	
2	A	(1,2)	3	1	3.5	10	3.25	3	
3	B	(1,5)	1	0.5	1.2	2	1.6	1	
4	C	(1,3)	5	3	9	18	4.5	3	
5	D	(2,5)	1	0.7	1	2	3.33	1	
6	E	(3,4)	6	3	20	50	10	3	
7	F	(4,5)	1	0.5	2.2	3	1.6	0.5	
8	G	(5,6)	2	1	4	9	5	1	
9	H	(6,7)	8	6	100	150	25	6	
10									
11	node	ti		T=	17				
12	1	0		Co=	1000				
13	2	3		Cp=	2000				
14	3	3		F=	5000				
15	4	6		y=	0				
16	5	6.5							
17	6	7.5							
18	7	13.5							
19									
20									
21	Objective Function:			18877					
22									
23	Constraints:								
24									
25	set (1):		CTij	<=	Xij	<=	NTij		
26	A	(1,2)	1	<=	3	<=	3		
27	B	(1,5)	0.5	<=	1	<=	1		
28	C	(1,3)	3	<=	3	<=	5		
29	D	(2,5)	0.7	<=	1	<=	1		
30	E	(3,4)	3	<=	3	<=	6		
31	F	(4,5)	0.5	<=	0.5	<=	1		
32	G	(5,6)	1	<=	1	<=	2		
33	H	(6,7)	6	<=	6	<=	8		
34									
35	set (2):		tj-ti	>=	Xij				
36	A	(1,2)	3	>=	3				
37	B	(1,5)	6.5	>=	1				
38	C	(1,3)	3	>=	3				
39	D	(2,5)	3.5	>=	1				
40	E	(3,4)	3	>=	3				
41	F	(4,5)	0.5	>=	0.5				
42	G	(5,6)	1	>=	1				
43	H	(6,7)	6	>=	6				
44									
45	3		y	>=	(tn-T)		y	>=	0
46			0	>=	-3.5		0	>=	0
47									
48	4		t1	>=	0				
49			0	>=	0				

11.9 (a)

Activity	(i,j)	d_{ij}	t_i	T_j	TS_{ij}	FS_{ij}
A	(1,2)	6	0	6	0	0
B	(2,3)	2	6	11	3	0
C	(3,5)	12	8	23	3	0
D	(2,4)	8	6	14	0	0
E	(2,6)	7	6	14	1	1
D_1	(4,5)	0	14	23	9	9
D_2	(4,6)	0	14	14	0	0
F	(5,7)	16	20	39	3	3
G	(4,7)	23	14	39	2	2
H	(6,7)	25	14	39	0	0
I	(7,8)	4	39	43	0	0

Critical path: A-D-D_2-H-I or 1-2-4-6-7-8; let X_8 denote the critical path

Earliest expected completion time, $E[X_8]$ = 43 days

(b) $E[X_8] = 43$, $V[X_8] = 31$

$P(X_8 \leq 45) = P(Z_8 \leq 0.36) = 0.64$

(c) Compress D one day, which increases cost by $175.

(d) Crash D two days (to 6) and E one day (to 6), which increases cost by $450.

(e) Thirty-seven days at a cost increase of $2,580. Note the large cost increase to reduce from 38 to 37 days.

Step	Action	Critical path(s)	Total cost increase	Earliest completion time
1	Compress D	$A-D-D_2-H-I$ $A-E-H-I$	$175	42
2	Crash D Crash E	$A-D-D_2-H-I$ $A-E-H-I$	$275 $450	41
3	Compress H	$A-D-D_2-H-I$ $A-E-H-I$ $A-B-C-F-I$	$750	40
4	Crash B Compress H	$A-D-D_2-H-I$ $A-E-H-I$ $A-B-C-F-I$ $A-D-G-I$	$800 $1,100	39
5	Compress C Crash G Crash H	As in step 4	$1,180 $1,280 $1,580	38
6	Crash I		$2,580	37

11.10 (a) The total direct cost equals the summation of the normal cost of all activities; that is, $26,200.

(b)

| Week | Early start | | Late start | |
	Weekly flow	Cumulative flow	Weekly flow	Cumulative flow
1	$2,200	$2,200	$1,000	$1,000
2	2,200	4,400	2,200	3,200
3	2,200	6,600	2,200	5,400
4	3,200	9,800	2,200	7,600
5	3,200	13,000	2,200	9,800
6	2,200	15,200	2,200	12,000
7	6,000	21,200	2,200	14,200
8	2,200	23,200	3,000	17,200
9	2,000	25,200	3,000	20,200
10	1,000	26,200	6,000	26,200

(c) The implication is clear if we compare the early-start cash flow and the late-start cash flow to each other and to a theoretical linear cash flow as follows. The results are given in the following table.

Week	Early-start cumulative flow	Late-start cumulative flow	Linear flow
1	$2,200	$1,000	$2,620
2	4,400	3,200	5,240
3	6,600	5,400	7,860
4	9,800	7,600	10,480
5	13,000	9,800	13,100
6	15,200	12,000	15,720
7	21,200	14,200	18,340
8	23,200	17,200	20,960
9	25,200	20,200	23,580
10	26,200	26,200	26,200

The early-start cumulative flow is lower than the linear flow for weeks 1 - 6 and is higher than the linear flow for weeks 7 - 10. The late-start cumulative flow is lower than the early-start cumulative flow and the linear flow throughout the project. Therefore, to minimize costs, a late start schedule should be adopted.

11.11 (a)

Duration	Activities to crash	Added costs	Total direct costs
10	–	–	$26,200
9	A	$1,500	$27,700
8	D,B	$3,000	$30,700
7	D,B	$3,000	$33,700
6	D,F	$3,500	$37,200

(b) Six weeks is the shortest completion time. Bottleneck activities are: A,B,F,E. In other words, all paths are critical.

11.12 (a) The managerial fee for the project is calculated by the following equation:

$$MF = 1,400 \times T$$

where T is the duration. The total cost computations as a function of project duration are summarized below.

Duration, T	Total direct cost	Managerial fee, MF	Total cost
10	$26,200	$14,000	$40,200
9	$27,700	$12,600	$40,300
8	$30,700	$11,200	$41,900
7	$33,700	$9,800	$43,500
6	$37,200	$8,400	$45,600

From the table, we see that the optimal duration is 10 weeks. It is only economically justified to reduce project duration when the additional crashing cost is less than the managerial fee.

(b) The additional cost to complete the project within 8 weeks is $41,900 – $40,200 – $1,700. Therefore, it is a justified cost to crash the project because the net profit will be $5,000 – $1,700 = $3,300.

11.13 Variance in activity durations (especially activities that are likely to be on the critical path) generates a variance in the completion time of the project. Although the total direct cost is not affected by the project's duration, the managerial fee is so the total cost is also a function of the project's duration.

11.14 (a)

Week, T	A. Direct weekly cash flow	B. Total weekly cash flow
1	$1,000	$3,000
2	$2,200	$4,200
3	$2,200	$4,200
4	$2,200	$4,200
5	$2,200	$4,200
6	$2,200	$4,200
7	$2,200	$4,200
8	$3,000	$5,000
9	$3,000	$5,000
10	$6,000	$8,000

Column A is the cash flow associated with the late-start schedule given in solution to Exercise 11.10b.

Column B = Column A + $2,000 managerial fee

(b) Because it is desired to increase the probability that the project will be completed on schedule, an early-start approach should be followed. Column A in the table below is taken from the solution to Exercise 11.10b and column B was generated by adding the weekly managerial fee of $2,000.

Week	A. Direct weekly cash flow	B. Total weekly cash flow
1	2,200	4,200
2	2,200	4,200
3	2,200	4,200
4	3,200	5,200
5	3,200	5,200
6	2,200	4,200
7	6,000	8,000
8	2,000	4,000
9	2,000	4,000
10	1,000	3,000

11.15 Consider two solution approaches:

    i. Constant resource usage (all activities performed in mode I to save resources).

Day	Activities performed	Mode	Resource I hours	Resource II hours
1	A,D	1	2	5.5
2	A,D	1	2	5.5
3	C,D	1	4	4
4	B,C	1	5	3
5	B,C	1	5	3
6	B,C	1	5	3
7	C	1	2	1
8	D	1	4	3
9	D	1	4	3
10	E	1	4	3

    ii. Minimizing the duration of the project (critical activities performed in mode 2, other activities performed in mode 1).

Day	Activity (mode)	Resource I hours	Resource II hours
1	A(2)	12	7
2	B(1),C(2),D(1)	9	9
3	B(1),C(2),D(1)	9	9
4	B(1),C(2),D(1)	9	9
5	C(2)	4	4
6	E(2)	9	5
7	F(2)	4	3

The total cost of each schedule is as follows:

Schedule	Cost of activities	Overhead	Total cost
i	$880	$1,500	$2,380
ii	$1,170	$1,050	$2,220

→ Schedule ii minimizes the total cost of the project.

11-16 Weekly labor cost per employee is $1,200 \times 1.25 = \$1,500$

(a, b)

Week	Early start			Late start		
	Labor	Weekly cost	Cumulative cost	Labor	Weekly cost	Cumulative cost
1	9	$13,500	$13,500	4	$6,000	$6,000
2	9	13,500	27,000	4	6,000	12,000
3	6	9,000	36,000	9	13,500	25,500
4	6	9,000	45,000	9	13,500	39,000
5	10	15,000	60,000	5	7,500	46,500
6	10	15,000	75,000	5	7,500	54,000
7	12	18,000	93,000	5	7,500	61,500
8	12	18,000	111,000	5	7,500	69,000
9	12	18,000	129,000	5	7,500	76,500
10	11	16,500	145,500	5	7,500	84,000
11	14	21,000	166,500	13	19,500	103,500
12	14	21,000	187,500	13	19,500	123,000
13	14	21,000	208,500	15	22,500	145,500
14	14	21,000	229,500	15	22,500	168,000
15	8	12,000	241,500	15	22,500	190,500
16	8	12,000	253,500	14	21,000	211,500
17	8	12,000	265,500	14	21,000	232,500
18	8	12,000	277,500	14	21,000	253,500
19	8	12,000	289,500	14	21,000	274,500
20	6	9,000	298,500	14	21,000	295,500
21	8	12,000	310,500	10	15,000	310,500

(c) When the allocated budget is below the late-start cash flow line it will not be possible to complete the project on time unless more dollars are allocated to expedite activities.

(d) When the allocated budget is above the early-start cash flow line there is excess cash that may be used for other purposes.

CHAPTER

12. PROJECT CONTROL

12.1 A project control system for the National Institutes of Health (NIH).

   (a) The objectives of the control system are as follows.

1. Monitor the progress of projects supported by NIH
2. Detect deviations in schedule, cost and expected performance
3. Forecast expected total cost and completion of projects
4. Support decision making regarding termination of projects
5. Support project evaluation, including decisions for new funding and extensions of existing projects

   (b) The performance measure for cost and schedule are based on the earned value logic where BCWP is measured in terms of activities completed satisfactorily (the length of each activity should be about 1 month).

   (c) A schedule and budget are required for each new project. A monthly report for each project indicates actual cost of each activity and its status. The earned value of an activity takes the following values:

0   = not started
0.5 = started not finished
1   = finished

   (d) For this system, the raw data include the actual cost for each activity (from the accounting system) and its status (see part *c* above) reported by the person responsible for it.

   (e) The earned value analysis should be used. This includes computations of variances and indexes for time and cost at each level of the OBS and WBS, as well as estimates for the budget at completion and the project completion dates.

   (f) A monthly report should be issued indicating all activities that are more than 20% over budget or 20% beyond schedule along with a plan on how to correct the situation and a forecast for next month's performance.

12.2 Input data for problem:

TABLE 12.12

Activity	Scheduled start day	Scheduled finish day	Cost/day
A	1	3	$1000
B	1	5	5000
C	3	7	3000
D	5	15	1000
E	7	22	2000
F	7	25	4000

A cost schedule control system produces weekly reports. The reports for weeks 1, 2 and 3 (assume 5 working days each week) are shown Table 12-13.

TABLE 12.13

Activity	Week 1 Status	Week 1 Cost	Week 2 Status	Week 2 Cost	Week 3 Status	Week 3 Cost
A	In process	$1,500	Finished	$3,000	Finished	$3,000
B	In process	$25,000	Finished	$30,000	Finished	$30,000
C	In process	$7,000	Finished	$10,000	Finished	$10,000
D	Not started	0	In process	$5,000	In process	$7,000
E	Not started	0	Not started	0	In process	$10,000
F	Not started	0	In process	$10,000	In process	$20,000

(a)   The following weekly report is based on cost and schedule performance measures as defined below. The "Cost" column reflects the actual cost to date divided by the original budget; the "Schedule" column reports the portion of work that has already been completed. As more detailed information becomes available, these calculations can be refined.

Activity	Week 1 Cost	Week 1 Schedule	Week 2 Cost	Week 2 Schedule	Week 3 Cost	Week 3 Schedule
A	$1500/3000 = 0.5$	$0.5/1 = 0.5$	$3000/3000 = 1$	$1/1 = 1$	1	1
B	$25000/25000 = 1$	$0.5/1 = 0.5$	$30000/25000 = 1.2$	$1/1 = 1$	1.2	1
C	$7000/21000 = 0.33$	$0.5/0.5 = 1$	$1000/21000 = 0.48$	$1/1 = 1$	0.476	1
D	–	–	$5000/10000 = 0.5$	$0.5/0.5 = 1$	$7000/1500 = 0.4$	$0.5/1 = 0.5$
E	–	–	–	$0/0.5 = 0$	$10000/44000 = 0.23$	$0.5/0.5 = 1$
F	–	–	$10000/30000 = 0.33$	$0.5/0.5 = 1$	$20000/10000 = 0.2$	$0.5/0.5 = 1$

Legend

Cost performance measure: Cumulative actual cost / cumulative planned cost

Schedule performance measure: % of activity completed / % of activity scheduled for completion

Completion of activities: 0 = not started
0.5 = started not finished
1 = finished

In this system, a time performance measure smaller than 1 indicates a schedule overrun and a cost performance measure larger than 1 indicates a budget overrun.

(b)   Due to the lack of earned value (BWP) estimates a clear picture is obtained only when each activity is completed (BCWP=100%). For in process activities a clear problem exists if the scheduled finish time has past, or actual cost exceed the budgeted cost of the activity.

12.3 Continuation of Exercise 12.2 with updated completion data

(a)   Given the new information, a comparison can be made between the actual % completed with the planned values. Also, a comparison between actual cost and planned cost for the work completed is possible.

Week 1

Activity	% complete	Actual cost	% planned	Planned cost	Cost perf.	Schedule perf.
A	50	$1,500	100	$1,500	1	0.5
B	30	$25,000	100	$7,500	3.33	0.3
C	10	$7,000	42	$2,100	0.33	0.24
D	0	0	7	0	0	NA
E	0	0	0	0	NA	NA
F	0	0	0	0	NA	NA

Cost performance measure = cumulative actual cost / cumulative planned cost for the work done

Schedule performance measure = % of activity completed / % of activity scheduled to be completed

Week 2

Activity	% complete	Actual cost	% planned	Planned cost	Cost perf.	Schedule perf.
A	100	$3,000	100	$3,000	1	1
B	100	$30,000	100	$25,000	1.25	1
C	100	$10,000	100	$21,000	0.48	1
D	20	$5,000	66	$3,000	1.66	0.3
E	0	0	45	0	NA	0
F	30	$10,000	40	$30,000	0.33	0.75

Week 3

Activity	% complete	Actual cost	% planned	Planned cost	Cost perf.	Schedule perf.
A	100	$3,000	100	$3,000	1	1
B	100	$30,000	100	$25,000	1.25	1
C	100	$10,000	100	$21,000	0.48	1
D	60	$7,000	100	$9,000	0.77	0.6
E	25	$10,000	68	$11,000	0.9	0.37
F	40	$20,000	60	$40,000	0.5	0.66

(b)   The estimated 'percent complete' serves as a baseline for comparison. Both the cost performance measure and the schedule performance measure are improved by using the new data. This is the logic of earned value systems.

12.4   An activity on the critical path of a project was scheduled to be completed within 12 weeks, with a budget of $8000. During a performance review, which took place 7 weeks after the activity was initiated, it was found that 50% of the work had already been completed and that the actual cost was $4,500.

(a) The earned value of the activity is 50% of $80 or $4,000.

(b) BCWS = $8,000(7/12) = $4,666
BCWP = $4,000
ACWP = $4,500
Cost index = BCWP / ACWP = 0.888
Schedule index = BCWP / BCWS = 0.857

(c) I. Based on the original estimate, the budget for the work remaining is

$$0.5 \times \$8,000 = \$4,000$$

ACWP is $4,500, thus the expected budget at completion is $4,000 + $4,500 = $8,500

(d) There are at least two ways to compute the expected budget at completion using the revised estimate approach:

II. The first is to revise the estimate for the work remaining based on past performance:

Revised budget for work remaining	$4500
ACWP	$4500
Expected budget at completion	$9000

III. The second is the optimistic approach; i.e., assume that the budget overrun will be corrected in the future and use the original cost estimate for this activity → $8000.

(e) Each of the three estimates is based on an assumption:

I. Although past cost performance did not match the original estimate, the remaining work will come in on budget as originally planned.

II. Past performance is the best indication of future performance. Thus if 50% of the work costs $4500 the remaining 50% will cost the same.

III. A budget overrun in the past is not an indication of future cost performances.

If the reason for the past cost overrun can be identified and treated then I is a good assumption. If the exact reason is not known, II is the best approach. Only if the reason is known and a detailed plan can be developed to complete the activity within the limits of its original budget may approach III be valid.**12.5 Original data:**

TABLE 12-15

Activity	Immediate predecessors	Normal time	Budget	Organization unit	Percent complete	Money spent
A	–	4	$90	U1	100	$110
B	A	2	$35	U2	100	$20
C	A	6	$75	U2	40	$40
D	B	3	$60	U1	80	$90
E	C	10	$80	U1	0	0
F	–	2	$40	U2	100	$40
G	F	5	$55	U1	50	$30
H	F	7	$80	U2	100	$60
I	D, E, G	1	$40	U2	0	0
J	H	10	$100	U1	0	0

(a)   Gantt chart for early-start schedule:

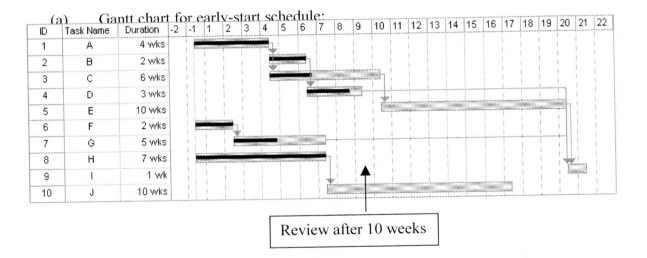

Review after 10 weeks

The emboldened lines denote the portion of work that has been completed after 10 weeks. Looking at the chart it becomes obvious that the progress is not satisfactory; however, it does not provide any information concerning budget utilization.

(b) and (c) Computation of SI and CI.

Activity	Budget	Org. unit	% complete	ACWP	BCWP	BCWS
A	$90	U1	100	$110	$90	$90
B	35	U2	100	20	35	35
C	75	U2	40	40	30	75
D	60	U1	80	90	48	60
E	80	U1	0	0	0	0
F	40	U2	100	40	40	40
G	55	U1	50	30	27.5	55
H	80	U2	100	60	80	80
I	40	U2	0	0	0	0
J	100	U1	0	0	0	10
Total	$655			$390	$350.5	$445
U1	$385			$230	$165.5	$215
U2	$270			$160	$185	$230
Total = U	$655			$390	$350.5	$445

$$SI = \frac{SV}{BCWS} = \frac{BCWP - BCWS}{BCWS}, \quad CI = \frac{CV}{BCWP} = \frac{BCWP - ACWS}{BCWP}$$

	SI	CI
U	-0.21	-0.11
U1	-0.23	-0.39
U2	-0.20	$+0.13$

The project as a whole is lagging behind the schedule and is 11% over budget. The bright stop is that organization unit U2 is 13% under budget.

(d) Update of completion time. Although 21% of the scheduled work content has not yet been completed, it is incorrect to assume that this number represents a schedule delay. For estimating delays, the critical path should be reviewed. In this case, activity C, which is on the critical path, has been delayed by 60%, or 0.6×6 weeks = 3.6 weeks.

Now, the expected completion time depends on the scenario that the project manager feels is the most appropriate. Two possible assumptions are:

1. The delay is a one-time occurrence so project completion will be delayed by 3.6 weeks.

2. The delay is representative of future delays of critical activities performed by U2. Now, the remaining activities are C, which is 40% complete, and activity I, which is 0% complete. If the same scheduling inefficiencies

experienced up until now are applicable in the future, then the remaining duration is

$$(3.6 \text{ wk} + 1 \text{ wk}) \times \frac{100}{40} = 11.5 \text{ weeks}$$

But because activity I has not yet commenced, the net delay is $11.5 - 1 = 10.5$ weeks.

Update of expected budget

Approach I: Assume a one-time cost overrun that will not be repeated. Looking at the above table we note that the "sunk" cost is equal to ACWP – BCWP = $390 –$350.5 = $39.5. If the project progresses according to the original schedule from this point on, the sunk cost can be viewed as the amount by which the budget has been exceeded. Therefore,

New Budget = Original Budget + Overrun

= $655 + $39.5 = $694.5

Approach II: The past is a good predictor of future performance. Noting that CI is the variance from the plan, we have

New Budget = (Original Budget) $\times$ (1 + CI) = $655 \times (1 + 0.11) = $727

12.6 For the project described in Exercise 12.5, calculate and chart the following values: BCWS, BCWP, ACWP. Assume linearity of cost versus time.

The following table provides the computations for BCWS.

Week	Activities	Weekly budget	Cumulative BCWS
1	A,F	$90/4 + $40/2 = $42.5	$42.5
2	A,F	$42.5	$85
3	A,G,H	$90/4 + $55/5 + $80/7 = $45	$130
4	A,G,H	$45	$175
5	B,C,G,H	$35/2 + $75/6 + $55/5 + $80/7 = $52	$227
6	B,C,G,H	$52	$279
7	C,D,G,H	$75/6 + $60/3 + $55/5 + $80/7 = $55	$334
8	C,D,H	$44	$378
9	C,D,H	$44	$422
10	C,J	$75/6 + $100/10 = $22.5	$445

Combining these results with the data in the table in the solution to parts (b) and (c) in Exercise 12.5, the cumulative curves for BCWS, BCWP, ACWP are given in the figure below

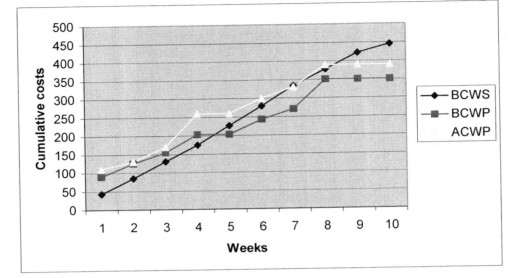

12.7 – 12.9 No solutions.

CHAPTER

13. RESEARCH AND DEVELOPMENT PROJECTS

13.1 – 13.4 No solutions.

13.5   As an example of a parallel funding problem, consider the flat-plate photovoltaic solar module project discussed by Bard (1985). At each of the three stages, a zero cost default option was available corresponding to the manufacturing capabilities at the time. The first stage, silicon purification, admitted two possible tasks, the first with two possible funding levels. The same situation existed at the second stage, cell purification. At the third stage only one task at one funding level was available. Input random variables included the incremental unit production cost at stage i denoted by w_i ($i = 1, 2, 3$) and a general efficiency factor, w_4, determined at stage 2. The output random variable at stage i for the jth task was computed from the expression $z_{ij} = w_i/w_4$ for a particular funding level. To conduct the analysis, it was necessary to estimate the cumulative distribution functions, $G_i(w_i)$ for each w_i and then derive the CDFs for each z_{ij}. Because the objective was to minimize expected utility, it was also necessary to assess a utility function for the total cost, z, of the project.

13.6   In the parallel funding network shown in Fig. 13.2, each arc represents a specific task whose outcome is a random variable, z_i, characterized by a derived probability distribution. Bard (1985) developed a mathematical programming model for this problem and used a combination of dynamic programming and simulation to find approximate solutions. A simplified version of the model follows.

Let s be the number of stages and r_i be the number of investment alternatives at stage i in increasing order of cost, C_i. Define a 0-1 decision variable u_{ij} to represent subset j ($j = 1, ..., r_i$) of investment alternatives at stage i, and let y_i ($y_i = 0, 1, 2, ...$) correspond to a particular investment level and hence, a particular value of u_{ij}. The problem of minimizing expect cost is

$$\min \sum_{i=1}^{s} E[z_i(y_i)]$$

$$\text{subject to} \quad \sum_{i=1}^{s} C_i(y_i) \leq B$$

$$g_k(\mathbf{u}, \mathbf{C}) \leq 0 \qquad k = 1, ..., m$$

$$y_i = y_i(u_i) \in \{0, 1, ..., r_i\} \quad i = 1, ..., s$$

where $z_i = \min\{z_{ij} : j = 1, ..., r_i\}$ and each z_{ij} is a function of a set of problem-specific input random variables, w_i, such as cost and efficiency (as noted in the solution to Exercise 13.5); $C_i(y_i)$ is a nonlinear cost function for stage i; B is the budget; and $g_k(\mathbf{u}, \mathbf{C})$ is a nonlinear function of the decision vector $\mathbf{u}$ and the cost vector $\mathbf{C}$ that accounts for collective task restrictions, such as the need to fund a particular series of tasks across two or more stages at a given level. It may also represent specific limitations on certain funding schemes, such as restricting the total dollar value of an award to a particular contractor.

13.7 No solution.

13.8

Sources of Information for Early Warning Signals†

Key variable	Internal source	External source
1. Positive chance event	None	News item
2. Produce life-cycle stage	None	Market analysis
3. Pressure on project leader	Missed deadlines, meetings with higher management, memos from higher management	None
4. R&D manager is project champion	Frequency project mentioned by higher management	None
5. Probability of commercial success	Marketing staff, operations staff	
6. Top management support	Access to top management, interest of top management	None
7. Project personnel commitment	Absenteeism, overtime and week-end work, group cohesiveness	None
8. Smoothness of technological route	Progress reports, clarity of benchmarks, attainment of milestones	Technical literature, professional conferences
9. End user market	Design changes, specification changes	None
10. Project champion appearing towards end	Reduction in cost and schedule overruns	None
11. Company profitability	Financial reports	Stock price fluctuations, P/E ratio
12. Anticipated competition	None	Trade shows, inside market information
13. Presence of internal competition	Movement of personnel, group formation, cross-membership	None
14. Number of projects in R&D portfolio	Company reports, R&D budget	None

†Adapted from Balachandra (1989)

13.9 – 13.10 No solutions.

CHAPTER

14. COMPUTER SUPPORT FOR PROJECT MANAGEMENT

The following references are the basis of the solutions.

Liberatore, M. J. and B. Pollack-Johnson, "Factors Influencing the Usage and Selection of Project Management Software," *IEEE-Transactions*, Vol. 50, No. 2, pp. 164-172 (May 2003).

Wohlin, C., A. von Mayrhauser, M. Host and B. Regnell, "Subjective Evaluation as a Tool for Learning from Software Project Process," *Information and Software Technology*, Vol. 42, No. 14, pp. 983-992 (November 2000).

Maxwell, K., Luk Van Wassenhove and Soumitra Dutta, "Performance Evaluation of General and Company Specific Models in Software Development Effort Estimation," *Management Science*, Vol. 45, No. 6, pp. 787-803 (June 1999).

Essex, D. E. "A Project for the Enterprise," *PM Network* (December 2003) (http://www.pmi.org/info/PIR_PMNetSoftware.pdf).

"NASA Selects PM Software" (http://www.pmforum.org/pmwt01/education01- 11.htm).

Ahmed, S. M., Lee Kam Fai and D. Darshi de Saram, "Project Management Software Selection Criteria in the Hong Kong Construction Company" (http://www.bre.polyu.edu.hk/crc/incite2000/Theme4/001.doc).

http://www.nwbuildnet.com/stores/ss/bci/compare.html

http://www.alexanderandzaia.com/home.htm

http://www.criticaltools.com/wbsmain.htm

http://www.criticaltools.com/pertmain.htm

http://www.guysoftware.com/planbee.htm

http://instruct.uwo.ca/gplis/640/mdustow/project.htm

14.1 Microsoft Project Report

1. General

  (a) *Product*

  Project management software: Microsoft product for windows MS Project

  (b) *System Requirements*
  - *Operating System*: Windows 3.x
  - *CPU type*: PC using 386 or higher compatible microprocessor
  - *Memory*: 4MB RAM
  - *Graphics*: EGA or higher resolution monitor
  - *Hard Drive*: 8MB of hard disk space
  - *Other*: Mouse or Windows pointing device

  (c) *Pricing*
  - MS Project can be purchased for approximately $469.00 US
  - Off-line technical support is available for $35

  (d) *Software Quality*

  1. *Software capabilities.* Project management programs provide a single interface to track and manage the resources, personnel, and decisions taken to reach a goal. As one of its components, MS Project includes fairly complete tools for scheduling tasks. Users can input durations down to the minute, place constraints on start and finish dates, and calculate schedules by specifying either "as soon as possible" or "as late as possible." Users can also schedule recurring tasks and set priorities on tasks. MS Project offers tracking flexibility by letting users set up to six baseline schedules per project. This capability enables more efficient what-if analysis and provides alternative views of progress. MS Project also supports extensive sorting and filtering options on reports and provides handy calendar reports that display task assignments and progress in a familiar format.

  With regard to resource management, MS Project can assign codes to costs and budgets to accounts. It can also assign resources more than once to the same task and highlight how resources have been allocated.

  One of Project 4.0's innovations lies in team communications and programmability. It offers a set of tools to keep everyone involved in a project up to date. It can also automatically generate e-mail messages informing members of a resource pool of their task assignments. Moreover, MS Project has editing and charting capabilities that allows the user to interface with Microsoft's Visual Basic for Applications for macro programming. Integration with other Microsoft Office applications is achieved via OLE support and users can link cost and resource details in Excel files to projects and task data in MS Project.

2. *Ease of use.* For years, project management software was so difficult to learn and use that its benefits were accessible only to specialists. Aimed at mainstream business users, MS Project includes on-line assistance features to help novices deal with the inherent complexities of project management. The interface resembles that of Word, Excel and PowerPoint, with customizable tool bars, menus and tabbed dialog boxes. The Calendar view provides an intuitive layout as an alternative to the more esoteric PERT and Gantt charts. Features that ease learning include Cue Cards, which offer detailed step-by-step instructions for performing common tasks; Planning wizard, which watches over users' actions, points out shortcuts and suggestions, and Charting Wizard, which generates charts automatically from questionnaire responses.

3. *Documentation and on-line help.* The Microsoft Project User's Guide includes information on how to get started, the project planning process, MS Project tools, appendixes, glossary, and an index. It provides conceptual information for more advanced topics, along with cross-references to specific on-line Cue Card procedures. MS Project also offers on-line assistance. The tutorial, Help system, Cue Cards, and on-line files make up the on-line documentation set.

4. *Training and technical support.* Microsoft Solution Providers are independent organizations that provide consulting, integration, customization, development, technical support and training, and other services for Microsoft products. Microsoft's Support On-line makes it easier to search Microsoft Technical Support's entire collection of problem-solving tools and technical information.

(e) *Discussion and recognition of advantages and disadvantages*

MS Project's Wizards and opening tutorial guide allow a user to create a simple project quickly with professional looking results. Gantt charts, PERT charts, calendars, wall charts, and detailed listings can all be produced using this program. In addition, task notes, and resource allocation and baseline views are helpful and useful. The detailed tasking helps the project manager organize the project and allocate team members. The flexibility and features of MS Project enables users to better manage and coordinate projects and the resources involved. Low-end packages, such as the one being discussed here, cost less than $500 and generally give a high benefit-cost ratio when compared with the competition.

14.2 Software Selection Methodology

General Knowledge: The purpose of project management software (PMS) is to facilitate the project management process and to support decisions making by the project manager. PMS products are often classified by their level of complexity with the more complex packages resulting in less ease of use. The most common classification scheme identifies three levels: low, medium, and high, although the differences between them may be blurred. There are many PMS packages available in the market and their successful implementation ultimately depends on suitability to the organizations' needs.

Step 1: Plan the project

Plan a software acquisition project to ensure that there is overall agreement on the objectives such as deliverables, scope, time frame, and approach for choosing the software. This should include the background on what type of tool you will be considering, why it is needed, and where it will fit in your technology architecture. You should also build the work plan that you will use to manage the project. This planning step takes place just as it would for any project that you manage.

Step 2: Gather and rank business requirements

It is difficult to select a tool or package if you are not sure what your requirements are. Again, this task involves the same type of analysis that is part of any project. Ask questions such as:

- What will people be using the package for?

- What problems will the package solve?

- What features and functions are required?

Many times you will not be able to determine all the requirements by just asking the customers. You can also look for other potential requirements by reviewing prior research from industry analysts, reading magazines and periodicals, and searching the web. These searches can be used to generate potential requirements that can be validated by your customers. Each requirement should be weighted on a qualitative scale—high/medium/low—to reflect the relative importance of some requirements over others. (Other weighting scales can be utilized as well.) All requirements and weighting schemes need to be reviewed and approved by your sponsor as well as major customers and stakeholders.

Step 3: Create an extensive list of packages

At this point, look for any and all packages that might meet your needs. This can be accomplished by searching the web, looking at trade magazines, talking to other companies, and do on. The purpose of the step is to gather a comprehensive, but not exhaustive, list of vendors and packages that warrant further consideration. If you think that you already know the particular packages you are interested in, this step can be skipped—moving directly to the short list. But this step helps ensure that there are no attractive candidates being overlooked.

Step 4: Create a short list of packages

Perform an initial, high-level evaluation of the long list, looking for obvious reasons to eliminate some of the alternatives. For example, certain products may not fit within your technology architecture, some may be too new and risky, or some may be too expensive. In some cases, there may be a feature that you absolutely need that is not available. The purpose of this step is create a short list of potential packages that look like they will have a reasonable chance of meeting your needs. If there are too many candidates on the list developed in Step 3 for you to evaluate personally, you could send a request for information (RFI) or a request for proposal (RFP) to each candidate for feedback. You could also ask for product brochures and other literature. In any case, the list of packages must be narrowed down to a small enough number so that a detailed comparative analysis can be conducted.

Step 5: Evaluate the short list of packages

This step can be the most difficult part of the selection process. You must map the package features and functions against your requirements and weighting factors to determine which package most closely meets your needs. If you did not send out an RFI or RFP at Step 4, you might want to send one out now for those candidates on the short list. You can also interview the vendors, set up product demonstrations, and make vendor site visits. Usually, some type of numerical calculation is made based on how well the package meets each requirement, multiplied by the weighting factor. Various approaches are discussed in Chapters 5 and 6. The package with the highest score across all requirements should be the one that best meets your needs. When you have completed this step, you should have a ranking of all the packages.

Step 6: Make the final selection and negotiate a contract
In many organizations, the project team makes the final recommendation and then turns the process over to the purchasing or procurement office. This office is responsible for contract negotiation and legal details.

Diagram of the selection of the most suitable PMS package process: The diagram below is based on the article "Project Management Software Selection Criteria in the Hong Kong Construction Industry" by S. M. Ahmed, Lee Kamfai and D. D. Desaram. The authors present results of a questionnaire survey conducted to ascertain which features were considered to be most important in the selection of software packages. The results were divided in two categories: (1) basic functions and (2) general system characteristics, and formed the basis for developing a methodology to selected a PMS package for use in the Hong Kong construction industry.

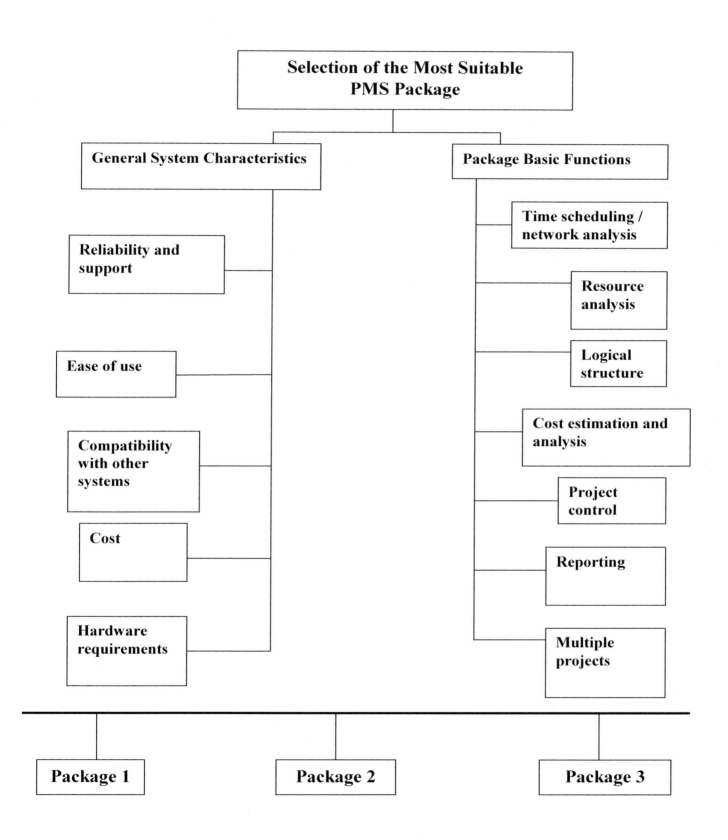

14.3 No solution.

14.4 Microsoft Project: Learning Time Evaluation

Overview of Microsoft Project (45 minutes)
- Menus
- Toolbars
- Getting Help within Microsoft Project
- Context Sensitive Help and Help Index
- Wizards

Scheduling (60 minutes)
- Creating Tasks and Milestones
- Defining Durations
- Creating Dependencies
- Entering Constraint Dates for Tasks
- Managing Schedule Conflicts
- Changing the Work Time (Calendars)
- Organizing a project using Outlining

Working with the Schedule (60 minutes)
- Using and defining Filters
- Changing Views
- Working with Tables
- Using the Global File and the Organizer to set standards and exchange Views

Resources (60 minutes)
- Defining Resources
- Assigning Resources
- Identifying Resource Conflicts using the many Resource Views
- Managing Resource Conflicts

Tracking Projects (30 minutes)
- Setting the Baseline
- Setting the Status Date
- Updating the Project
- Rescheduling the Project
- Comparing the Baseline Plan vs. the Current Plan

Reporting (45 minutes)
- Printing Views
- Printing Reports

Multi-Project Planning (60 minutes)
- Consolidating Project Schedules
- Integrating Multiple Projects (creating cross-project dependencies)
- Managing Resources across Multiple Projects (creating and using Resource Pools)

Total time evaluation is approximately 6 hours.

14.5 – 14.7   No solutions.

14.8   (a) Software Specifications (Microsoft Project)

- Tasks per project file
- Resources per project
- Resource units per assignment
- Task dependencies per project file
- Predecessors per task
- Successors per task
- Outline levels per project
- Consolidated projects
- Open project files per consolidated project
- Sharer files connected to a resource pool
- Open windows
- Base calendars
- Calendar exceptions per calendar
- Printable tasks in monthly calendar
- Rate tables to support different pay scales and rates (per resource)
- Variable rates per rate table to support rate increases and decreases
- Maximum cost value in a currency field
- Maximum work value (hours)
- Print scaling adjustment range percentage (percent)
- Page header text (lines)
- Page footer text (lines)
- Page legend text (lines)
- Page legend text box width (inches)
- Filter tests per filter
- Filter tests per AutoFilter (per column)
- Earliest date allowed for calculation
- Latest date allowed for calculation

(b.1) In general, most specifications related to any project management software package are similar, with the main differences being the specific values associated with potential users of the package. (Note that PMI has a "generic" list of specifications and criteria for PM software packages). For example, the specifications for *resource units per assignment* (e.g., 10,000) and *number of open windows* (e.g., 50) can have smaller values assuming that the project being managed in the course is below these limits. The main differences between packages will be in their features and the relative weights of the criteria used to select the appropriate software package to be used as a teaching aid. For example, the "ease of use" criterion should get greater weight in a software package used to support a course since most potential users are students who are probably not familiar with PM packages. The common feature "email" is not so important in this context because the teaching emphasis should be on the package and its capabilities. The students are not likely to need this feature when getting acquainted with the package.

(b.2) When the software package to be used for planning and controlling projects managed by your school, the specifications shouldn't be different than those were mentioned in part (b.1). Projects managed by a school can be the same size as projects that arise in organizations. The first step for selecting the appropriate software package is to plan the project; the second step is to gather and rank business requirements. At this point, the projects should be managed by the appropriate units in the school or organization. The general requirements of either are likely to have considerable overlap.

14.9 No solution.

14.10 "The purchase price of the project management software package is a negligible issue as long as the price is no more than a few thousand dollars." There are two ways of interpreting this statement:

a. the purchase price versus the other costs of the software package itself

b. the purchase price (and all the other costs of the package) versus the other costs of the projects being handled

In the article "Project management software selection criteria in the Hong Kong construction industry" by Syed M. Ahmed, Lee Kamfai and D. Darshi Desaram cited above, the authors present results of a questionnaire survey conducted to ascertain the features of PM software packages that are considered important. As part of the questionnaire, they also tried to identify the main selection criteria. The results are summarized in the following figure.

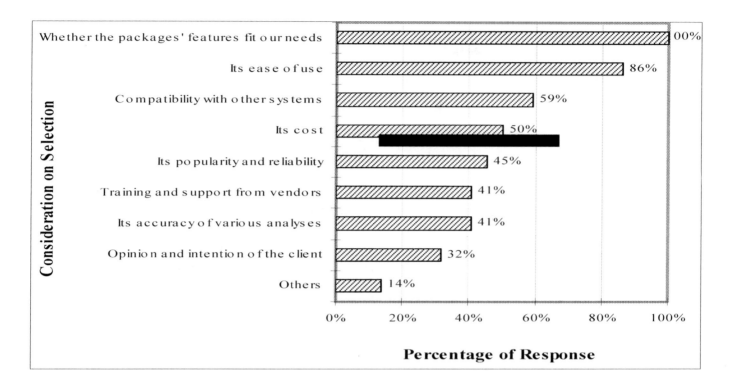

Conclusions: Of the respondents, 86% considered ease of use in the selection process, 59% considered compatibility with other systems, and 50% considered the cost. The immediate conclusion with respect to the exercise question is that the purchasing price of the PMS package is an important factor in the selection process. In addition, other cost factors, such as installing, maintaining and using the software should be taken into consideration besides the purchase price (see numeric example).

In today's competitive market, even the most profitable companies try to minimize their costs and return the maximum shareholder benefits, taking into account all expenses. As a result, the cost of purchasing a software package for a few thousand dollars is not a negligible issue.

Example: Purchase cost of software versus software life-cycle cost

Parameters:

C_1 = purchase cost per unit (quantity discount) ($5,500)

C_2 = hardware and facilities cost ($12,000)

C_3 = operations and maintenance cost ($2,000 per year)

C_4 = estimated value at phase-out (0)

C_5 = upgrading to latest version ($500 per year)

L = expected service life (5 years)

$$C_T = \text{total cost} = \sum_{i=1}^{5} C_i = \$30,000$$

Conclusions: If the total budget for the software life cycle (assuming a 5-year service life) is $30,000, then the purchase cost cannot be ignored.

14.11 As part of your company's effort to select a project management software package, you have been asked to approach several other companies that presently use such packages.

a. Questionnaire to help collect the relevant information:

Step 1 (Checking relevance) Because the selection process begins by identifying data processing needs, the first step is to check if the data processing needs are similar in both companies.

1. How many projects are usually managed in parallel? (mark your answer)
a. less than 10
b. 20 – 50
c. above 50

2. What is the project's duration?
a. less than a month
b. 1 to 6 months
c. above 6 months

3. How many different resources are needed?
a. less than 10
b. 10 –3 0
c. above 30

4. How many organizations usually participate in a typical project?
a. less than 3
b. 3 – 5
c. 6 – 8
d. above 8

Step 2 (Relative weights)

1. Write your estimation regarding the relative weights of the following components (total weight should summarize to 100)

1) Activities and scheduling _____

2) Budgeting and cost estimation _____

3) Resources _____

4) Project structure _____

5) Configuration management   ____

6) Project control   ____

7) Reporting   ____

8) General system characteristics   ____

Step 3 (Criteria's scoring)

- Write your company name   _____

- Write which software package you usually use   _____

- According to criteria list that was presented in step 2 write your score estimation for every criteria (on a 0 – 10 scale) according to the software package being used in your company:

  1) Activities and scheduling   ____

  2) Budgeting and cost estimation   ____

  3) Resources   ____

  4) Project structure   ____

  5) Configuration management   ____

  6) Project control   ____

  7) Reporting   ____

  8) General system characteristics   ____

Step 4 (Cost evaluation) The next 6 questions relate to the life-cycle cost of each package.

  1) Estimate the package's purchase cost (per unit, quantity discount)?   _____

  2) Estimate the package's hardware and facilities cost?   _____

  3) Estimate the package's operation and maintenance cost per year?   _____

  4) Estimate the package's expected service life?   _____

  5) Estimate the package's cost of updating and new versions?   _____

  6) Estimate value at phase out time?   _____

b. Fill out two questionnaires, each representing a different software package.

Let's say that the relative weights according to the "scoring model" are:

1) Activities and scheduling   __20__

2) Budgeting and cost estimation   __15__

3) Resources   __15__

4) Project structure   __10__

5) Configuration management   __10__

6) Project control   __10__

7) Reporting   __10__

8) General system characteristics   __10__

Now we score for the criteria:

Package 1:

1) Activities and scheduling   __6__

2) Budgeting and cost estimation   __7__

3) Resources   __7__

4) Project structure   __5__

5) Configuration management   __6__

6) Project control   __5__

7) Reporting   __4__

8) General system characteristics   __6__

Package 2:

1) Activities and scheduling   __8__

2) Budgeting and cost estimation   __7__

3) Resources   __6__

4) Project structure   __6__

5) Configuration management   __7__

6) Project control   __6__

7) Reporting   __8__

8) General system characteristics   __6__

Cost data for selection problem:

Package 1:

1) Estimate the package's purchase cost (per unit, quantity discount)? $450

2) Estimate the package's hardware and facilities cost? $600

3) Estimate the package's operation and maintenance cost per year? $1000/year

4) Estimate the package's expected service life? 4 years

5) Estimate the package's cost of updating and new versions? $300/year

6) Estimate value at phase-out? 0

Total cost package 1 (4 years) = $450 + $600 + 4 × $1,000 + 4 × $300 = $6,250

Package 2:

1) Estimate the package's purchase cost (per unit, quantity discount)? $900

2) Estimate the package's hardware and facilities cost? $700

3) Estimate the package's operation and maintenance cost per year? $1200/year

4) Estimate the package's expected service life? 4 years

5) Estimate the package's cost of updating and new versions? $300/year

6) Estimate value at phase out time? 0

Total cost package 2 (4 years) = $900 + $700 + 4 × $1,200 + 4 × $300 = $7,600

Now compute a cost-effectiveness ratio (points/$1,000)

= total points / (total cost/100)

Package 1: C-E ratio = 59 / 6.25 = 9.44

Package 2: C-E ratio = 68.5 / 7.6 = 9.01

Summary

Criteria	Weight	Package 1 score	Package 2 score
Activities and scheduling	20	12	16
Budgeting and cost estimation	15	10.5	10.5
Resources	15	10.5	9
Project structure	10	5	6
Configuration management	10	6	7
Project control	10	5	6
Reporting	10	4	8
General system characteristics	10	6	6
Total points	100	59	68.5
Total cost		$6,250	$7,600
Relative cost		100%	121.6%
C-E ratio (points/$1,000)		9.44	9.01

Conclusions: The results show that package 2 scores higher than package 1 on total points but ranks lower with respect to "resources" and "general system characteristics." The purchase cost of Package 1 is $450 lower than package 2 and the annual cost is $200 lower, however. In light of these statistics, the company should weigh package 2's higher cost against its superior performance. One way to do this is with the C-E ratio, which indicates that Package 1, with a score of 9.44 points per $1,000, is better than Package 2, whose score is 9.01 points per $1,000.

14.12 Evaluating project management software packages (The answers to this exercise are based on the authors' experience and their reading of the literature.)

a. Common features
- Budgeting and cost control
- Calendars
- Email
- Graphics
- Importing/exporting data
- Handling multiple projects and subprojects
- Report generation.
- Resource management
- Planning
- Project monitoring and tracking
- Scheduling
- Security
- Sorting and filtering
- What if analysis

   b. New features
- Perform multi-project managements tasks
- Use of the Web as a communication tool

   c. Leading packages: There are significant differences in the packages chosen by companies within and between industry groups. Companies in older industries with a strong history of project management (construction and engineering) making heavy use of the more high-end packages, give high scores to **Primavera**. (Note, software packages are categorized as either high-end or low-end, based on price. High-end packages cost $900 or more, while low-end packages cost $600 or less.) Companies in newer, more technology-oriented industries (computer software/data processing) making heavy use of the simple, less expensive package, give high scores to **Microsoft Project**. The main reasons for these preferences are:

- easy of use
- ability to integrate smoothly with other systems
- high benefit-cost ratio

   d. Important criteria
- Capacity
- Ease of use
- On-line help facilities

   e. Criteria suggestion
- Installation requirements
- Level of security
- Vendors support

THE RED FLAG CHANNEL
by
Zhang Xiang
College of Management
Huazhong University of Science and Technology, PRC

Introduction

The Red Flag Channel (RFC), built in the 1960s, is one of the great hydraulic projects of China. The purpose of the project was to divert water from the Zhuo-Zhang River in Shanxi Province to Lin County in Henan Province to solve the water shortage problem that had existed for thousands of years.

In the history of Lin County, the lack of water left many of the local inhabitants struggling for survival throughout most of their lives. In recent times it is said that the price of water has always been much higher than the price of oil. Out of a total of 550 administrative villages in the county, 305 had major water problems that required people to walk 3 to 5 km a day to satisfy their barest needs. According to the statistics from 1436 to 1949, Lin County was the victim of more than 100 natural disasters, 30 of which were droughts that left the land infertile for years.

Since 1957, several small hydraulic projects were undertaken in the county but the problem persisted due to the normal lack of rain and the absence of underground aquifers.

Detailed Technical Data for RFC

The proposed channel was designed to be more than 4100 km in length. To properly carry out the construction, the entire project was divided into 15 major sections and hundreds of small sections, including the assemble channel section, mainstream channel sections and Youth Tunnel section, to name a few. In addition, a project committee (very similar to a project office) was set up to coordinate all aspects of the project and ensure smooth construction. Under the project headquarters office, the following eight groups were created: an administrative group, a technical and engineering group, a propaganda and education group, a worker allocation and welfare group, a material supply group, a food supply group, a tools, transportation and telecommunication group, and a security and safety group.

The working and living conditions at that time were very difficult. Ninety-eight percent of the project was built in a mountainous area. However, the Chinese people overcame the many difficulties and successfully completed the project using little more than their bare hands. During the construction, 7747 of the 50,000 workers were trained in certain skills on site and promoted to leadership positions.

The project was started in February 1960. Although it was scheduled to be finished in May 1967, it wasn't actually completed until July 1969 because of the interruptions that resulted from the Cultural Revolution (i.e., the national disruptions and riots that took place in China between 1966 and 1976). The first flow of water into the assemble mainstream channel occurred on April 5, 1965. The other three mainstream channels were completed in April 1966. The branch channels, slots and ditches were completely in July 1969.

The assemble mainstream channel is 70.6 km long with a bottom width of 8 m and a wall height of 4.3 m. The slope is 1:8000 with a designed flow rate of 23 m^3/s. The entire section was built in the Taihang Mountain.

The assemble mainstream channel was divided into three mainstream channels at the watershed station. The first mainstream channel extends southwest and is 39.7 km long with a bottom width of 6.5 m and a wall height of 3.5 m. It has a slope of 1:5000 with a designed flow rate of 14 m^3/s. It can irrigate 234.4 million m^2 of farmland.

The second mainstream channel extends southeast and is 47.6 km long with a bottom width of 3.5m and a wall height of 2.5 m. It has a slope of 1:2000 with a designed flow rate of 7.7 m^3/s. It can irrigate 77.25 million m^2 of farmland.

The third mainstream channel heads east and is 10.9 km long with a bottom width of 2.5 m and a wall height of 2.2 m. Its slope is 1:3000 with a designed flow rate of 3.3 m^3/s. It can irrigate 30.6 million m^2 of farmland.

In addition to the assemble mainstream channel and three mainstream channels, there are 51 branch channels of 524.1 km length, 290 sub-branch channels of 697.3 km length, 4281 ditches and slots of 2488 km length, and 151 bridge-like slots of 12.5 km length. Also, 48 small reservoirs and 346 weirs and cofferdams were built on the channels. Finally, there are 211 tunnels, 53.7 km in total length.

To complete the project, a total of 56,110,000 person work-days were used from the local population. The amount of earth removed was 22,250,000 m^3 and the total investment was RMB 125.03 million, including RMB 46.25 million invested by the government and RMB 78.78 million invested by the local collectives (at the time, the exchange rate was: RMB 1 = USD 2.8.

Preparation before the Project

On October 10, 1959, Lin County gave its support to the project at the county meeting. Following the meeting, four site surveys and investigations were arranged by the county administrators.

The RFC report of Lin County was submitted to the Xinxiang Administration Area for approval on November 6, 1959.

The approval for the project was given by the Xinxiang Administration to Lin County on December 23, 1959. The report of Lin County was submitted to the Henan Province for coordination on January 16, 1960. The coordination letter was sent from Henan Province to Shanxi Province on January 27, 1960. A government reply letter from Shanxi Province was sent to Henan Province on February 3, 1960, agreeing to the project. The project committee was organized on February 7, 1960 in Lin County. The detailed arrangements (note that they did not use a WBS at that time) were scheduled in the form of the construction plan on February 7, 1960.

Youth Tunnel

The Youth Tunnel is one of the critical sections on the assemble mainstream channel and is located on a steep cliff composed of hard rocks. The tunnel is 616 m long, 5m high and 6.2m wide, and has a slope of 1:5000. The designed flow rate is 23 m^3/s. The amount of earth removed was 19,400 m^3 and required more than 130,000 person work-days.

Work on the tunnel was started in February 1960 and engaged 320 young workers who were selected from the local communities. In October of the same year, China was hit with a series of natural disasters causing the national economy to go into a deep depression. The food available for each worker on the site was less than 0.3 kg per day. Despite the very tough conditions, workers invented many new explosion methods and technologies, which improved the progress from 0.3 m/day to 2 m/day.

The tunnel was finally completed on July 15, 1961. To commemorate the spirit of those young people, the tunnel was named "Youth Tunnel."

Since its completion, the Red Flag Channel has been frequently shown to foreign visitors by Chinese senior officers. The late Premier Zhou proudly said to his foreign friends that the Red Flag Channel was one of the great miracles in China in the 1960s. Since then, it has received dozens of senior officer visits from the central government, including three presidents and three premiers.

Red Flag Channel Data Supplement

1. Overview Map of the Red Flag Channel

The total length of the Red Flag Channel is 1500 km, including the mainstream channel, the branch channels, ditches, and slots.

2. Schedule Deviation

According to the Initial Construction Arrangement Plan of the Red Flag Channel, drafted on February 7, 1960, the assemble mainstream channel originating from the Zhuo-Zhang River and extending to the watershed should have been finished by May 1, 1960. But this was soon realized by not to be a realistic goal, and in fact, it was not until April 5, 1965 that water first began to flow in this channel (the project was finished in July 1969).

In 1966, the project was disrupted by the Cultural Revolution. This resulted in a two-year delay, which was one of the reasons why the project was not completed until July 1969.

A second reason for the delay was the lack of experience in carrying out a hydraulic project of such magnitude. According to the "Historical Review of Red Flag Channel," authored by the former head of the county, Yang Gui, the 50,000-man workforce was organized along the full length of the channel from the very beginning, but they were thinly scattered so progress was slow. Several months into the project, the situation was realized and the schedule was revised to make it more realistic. The first step was to pool workers so that they could finish the 27 km section in Shanxi Province. After concentrating resources, progress was more rapid.

The third reason was inadequate equipment, poor working conditions, and primitive living standards. The only tools available were spades and hammers, the food supply was limited to 0.3 kg per day per worker, and shelter was either nonexistent or could only be found in caves. As one might expect, such conditions adversely affected progress.

The fourth reason for the delay was political. Disputes on whether to continue were constant throughout its life of the project, which was placed in the same category as a series of natural disasters that crippled the national economy in the 1960s. Some politicians agreed to the project because they believed that in the long run, it was the only solution to the water shortage problem. Others strongly disagreed, owing to the huge consumption of material and money. They believed that the project would have a further negative impact on the deeply depressed local economy.

3. Project Risks

According to the Initial Construction Arrangement Plan of the Red Flag Channel drafted dated February 7, 1960, the decision to go ahead with the project was based on three factors or advantages that foreshadowed its success. However, several risks were also identified.

The first advantage related to the national hydraulic policies and the support of the Chinese central government. The second advantage was the strong local demand for the project. The third advantage was the experience gained from hydraulic construction during 1958-1959.

The risks are summarized below.

1. *Natural risks.* Most of the construction was carried out in a mountainous area: 1250 hills and mountains had to be carved; 151 water slots had to be built to bridge the mountainous gaps; and 21 tunnels had to be dug to facilitate the water flow. The amount of earth removed could fill a structure 2 m in width, 3 m in height and over 2900 km—the distance from the south Chinese city of Guangzhou to the north city of Harbin.

2. *Technology risk.* The professional technicians were from other provinces and only temporary. Although they were the backbone of the project, they were small in number not hired for the full length of the project. Their primary role was to address major problems. As a consequence, the local workers were empowered to take responsibility for day-to-day operations and to overcome all kinds of difficulties. Many workers were found to be exceptionally talented, for example, inventing new ways to explode the steep cliffs and creating new methods to produce lime.

3. *Construction risk.* The construction facilities and equipment were at best rudimentary. The only tools the workers had were hammers, spades, and the like so most of the work was done manually. Looking back, it is now said that the entire channel was built with bare hands.

4. *Economic risk.* This was biggest risk at the time. Local populations did not think in terms of investing for the future but instead tried to save money by reducing administration expenses. When construction started, China had only RMB 2 million in cash and 20,000 tons of food in storage.

5. *Political risk.* As mentioned, squabbling among officials never stopped. The head of the county Yang Gui, as leader of the project, had been strongly criticized by some senior officers. Fortunately, the other officers and all local population gave their full support to the project because they believed that it would lead to a brighter future for those in the county. During the preparation stage, the late Chairman Mao ZeDong met with Yang Gui on November 1, 1958, to express his concerns. Later in 1970, when the project was finished, the late premier Zhou Enlai proudly introduced the Red Flag Channel to his foreign friends as one of the two great miracles of the 1960s in China. In addition, several senior provincial government officials gave their personal support to the project by contributing ideas to deal with the political disputes.

4. Benefits of the Red Flag Channel

As of April 2004, after 40 years of channel operation, it is clear that Lin County has benefited immensely from the project. A total of 8.5 billion cubic meters of water has flowed into the county and the long-standing water shortage problem has been solved for the 600,000 local inhabitants. Over 53,280,000,000 square meters of farmland have been irrigated, and farmers now have 1,590,000 tons more rice and corn on hand. The power supply from the channel has been more than 470,000,000 kW hours, and the total profit more than RMB 1.7 billion, which is 23 times the cost of the original investment taking inflation into account. In the last 10 years, the tourist income alone resulting from the Red Flag Channel has been over USD 10 million.

5. Limited Archives

Because of the tumultuous period in which the channel was built (the Cultural Revolution spanned 1966 to 1976), very limited documentation remains. According to recent articles, the vast majority of the construction drawings and work plans were lost over time. At least four reasons account for this loss: (1) the political convulsions at that time; (2) the absence of formal archival procedures and systems; and (3) the lack of storage facilities; and (4) a shortage of funds.

Critical Thinking
___

1. *Was the project a success despite the many difficulties and troubles during the whole construction period?*

2. *What lessons can we learn from this project?*

3. *Discuss project management "spirit." What can we learn from the project?*

4. *What contributed to the success of the project?*

Photographs from the Project

Red Flag Channel

On site

Channeling

On site

Channeling a cave

Different sections of the channel

Channel joint

Channel slots

Various channels

Head of county leads workforce

Finding a place on the cliffs for an explosion

Moving ahead

Cutting into the maintains

Working on site